Complete EnglishSmart

Grade **7**

Nicholas Adeyeye

Complete EnglishSmart Contents

Section 1

Integrated Practice

A Farewell to Pluto

Do you remember learning the names of the planets in our solar system when you were in elementary school? Maybe your parents quizzed you to help you remember them before a test. Or maybe you thought of a mnemonic (a memory helper) to help you remember them all – like this one:

My Very Easy Memory Jingle Seems Useful Naming Planets.

With this mnemonic, you could remember not only all the planets, but also the order of their locations from the Sun: Mercury, Venus, Earth, Mars, Jupiter, Saturn, Uranus, Neptune, and Pluto. But now, this mnemonic will no longer work. In August, 2006, the International Astronomical Union (IAU) declared that Pluto is no longer classified as a planet.

Pluto was discovered in 1930 by American astronomer Clyde Tombaugh, and its status as a planet had been debated for quite some time. Over the years, as telescope and space technologies improved, astronomers gained a better understanding of the outer extremities of our solar system. We now know, for example, that Pluto's orbit around the Sun is irregular, compared to the other planets. Moreover, astronomers have discovered several other celestial objects near Pluto that orbit the Sun and are the same size as Pluto. Measurements and pictures obtained from the Hubble Space Telescope show that one celestial body in the region is, in fact, larger than Pluto.

In 2006, when the IAU redefined the meaning of "planet", they created the following stipulations. A planet must: (1) orbit the Sun, (2) be large enough that its gravity pulls it into a relatively spherical shape, and (3) have a "clear neighbourhood" around its orbit. Because of its small size, its irregular orbit around the Sun, and the fact that there were other small celestial bodies near it, Pluto was reclassified as a "dwarf planet". There are now three "dwarf planets" in our solar system – Pluto, Ceres, and Eris.

You will need to relearn what you have been taught as a child about the planets of our solar system, but it won't be hard. When the declaration of Pluto losing its planet status

was made, people around the world reacted with nods of understanding and acceptance, howls of outrage, and shrugs of indifference.

Where do your feelings about dwarf planet Pluto fit in?

A. Answer these questions.

1. Why do you think astronomers had waited so long before declassifying Pluto as a planet?

   I think that they Waited so long before declassifying Pluto because they where not sure to do it.

2. What made the International Astronomical Union decide to take Pluto off the list of planets?

   What made them to be out Pluto was because pluto was small and that the celestial body in bigger than Pluto

3. How did people react to the IAU's decision?

   Some people were against it but some people accepted the desicion. and some people did not care.

4. Make up a mnemonic to help you remember the names of the Great Lakes: Lake Erie, Lake Huron, Lake Michigan, Lake Ontario, and Lake Superior.

   My Very Easy Memory Jingle Seems Useful For Naming The Great Lakes
   E
   E   Each   The
   H   Horse   Open
   M   Must
   S   Stagger
   In

Is the International Astronomical Union making the right move to declassify Pluto as a planet? Why or why not?

_____

_____

_____

_____

_____

B. Fill in the blanks with words from the passage.

Clyde Tombaugh, an American 1. _Astronomer_, 2. _discovered_ Pluto in 1930. Pluto was then classified as the ninth planet in the 3. _Solar_ system. In 2006, however, the International Astronomical Union (IAU) convened to debate over the 4. _Status_ of Pluto as a 5. _Planet_. The IAU finally decided to have Pluto 6. _____ as a 7. _____ planet. They gave three reasons for their decision. First, Pluto is too small. Second, it does not follow a regular path to 8. _Orbit_ the Sun. Third, it does not have a clear 9. _Neighbourhood_ around its orbit.

C. Complete the following.

1. "Astro" refers to things relating to the stars or to outer space.

   a. The branch of knowledge about the universe is _Astro_.

   b. A person who travels to space is an _astronaut_.

   c. A scientist who studies the universe is an _astronomer_.

2. "Tele" means "over a distance".

   a. A device for seeing faraway objects is a _telescope_.

   b. A device for receiving images over a distance is a _tele_.

   c. A device for talking to each other over a distance is a _telephone_.

3. "Inter" means "between two or more".

   a. The adjective _inter_ is used when different countries are involved.

   b. A competition among schools is an _inter_ competition.

   c. The students exchange their ideas about the play. They _interpret_ their ideas.

D. Read the clues and complete the crossword puzzle with words from the passage.

Across

A. the planet that is closest to the sun

B. smaller than normal

C. discussed

D. expresses anger or displeasure

E. round like a ball

F. where something is found

G. consider something in a new way

H. lack of interest

Down

1. anger
2. became aware of something
3. goodbye
4. a memory helper

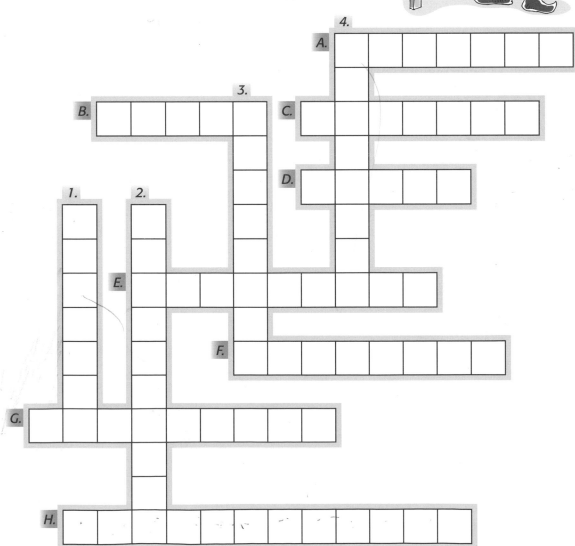

English –
a Language that Likes to Lend and Borrow

English words are often borrowed by other languages. In China, for example, young people say "hi" as much as *ni hao* and "baibai" as much as *xiajian*. Other popular English loan words are guitar (*jita*), chocolate bar (*qiaokeli ba*), cool (*ku*), and vitamin (*weitaming*). Of course, there are many more. But the English language also includes many words that come from other languages. Maybe you know some words and think they are English – when they are actually examples of words from other languages. Look at the list below of words that English speakers often use. Can you guess which languages they are borrowed from?

1. **Tsunami** – We used to say "tidal wave", but the word tsunami is being used more often now, because the term "tidal wave" is not an accurate description of what the surge of water is. Tides are related to the presence of the moon; tsunamis are formed by disturbances in the sea, such as earthquakes, meteors, or landslips that fall into bodies of water.

2. **Gung-ho** – This means "eager". Workers in the country where this term comes from used it as a working slogan.

3. **Karaoke** – If you like to do this activity, then you should at least know where the word comes from.

4. **Orangutan** – This is what we call the primates that live in Southeast Asia. In its native language, this word means "man of the jungle".

5. **Boondocks** – We use this word to describe a place that is far away and isolated. In its native language, it is *bundock*, meaning "mountain".

6. **Ketchup** – This word is what bottled tomato sauce is called in the United States. It also means tomato sauce – pronounced *ke jap* – in the country of its origin.

7. **Tattoo** – An English explorer named Captain Cook arrived at the place where tattoos were first done. That was 250 years ago. Now, tattoos are popular all over the world.

8. **Taboo** – If something is forbidden, we may call it "taboo". Captain Cook also "discovered" this word. We first learned about it from his Captain's journal.

9. **Chess** – No one is exactly sure where chess originated, but maybe the origin of this word offers us a definitive clue.

10. **Shampoo** – You may be surprised where this word comes from.

A. Guess and write the origin of each of the above words in the space provided below. Then check the answers at the bottom of this page to see if your guess is right.

1. _Japan_

2. _China_

3. _Japan_

4. _Asia_

5. _Phillipenos_

6. _China_

7. _united kingdom_

8. _tongan_

9. _Japan_

10. _Hindi_

B. Answer these questions.

1. Which of the above words did you think were English words? Why?

   Chess, Karoke, ketup, tattoo, Shampoo. because its normal english words we use.

2. Why do you think the English language has to borrow words from other languages?

   I think because before english only had a few words. So they had to borrow some forign words

3. Do you like to see more foreign words added to the English language? Why or why not?

   I dont think so because I think english has to have some own words made from that country

4. Do you think the English language will add more or fewer foreign words into its vocabulary? Why?

   I think it will add fewer foreing words because the english language already has enough words.

1. Japanese 2. Chinese (Mandarin) 3. Japanese 4. Bahasa Malaya 5. Filipino (Tagalog) 6. Chinese (Cantonese) 7. Tahitian 8. Tongan 9. Persian (Farsi) 10. Hindi

11

C. **Match the following borrowed words with their origins.**

Word

1. Taekwondo •
2. bazaar •
3. yacht •
4. rouge •
5. silk •
6. futon •
7. bamboo •
8. banana •
9. mammoth •
10. corridor •
11. algebra •
12. ski •
13. null •
14. cash •
15. vanilla •

Origin

• Malay
• Japanese
• Dutch
• Norwegian
• French
• Korean
• German
• Tamil
• Arabic
• Italian
• Spanish
• Persian
• Portuguese
• Russian
• Chinese

D. Find five more borrowed words. Explain their origins and what they mean. Use each of the words in a sentence of your own to show how it can be used.

1. Word: _____

   Explanation: _____

   _____

   Sentence: _____

2. Word: _____

   Explanation: _____

   _____

   Sentence: _____

3. Word: _____

   Explanation: _____

   _____

   Sentence: _____

4. Word: _____

   Explanation: _____

   _____

   Sentence: _____

5. Word: _____

   Explanation: _____

   _____

   Sentence: _____

THE SOUND OF MUSIC
The Story of Maria and Georg von Trapp

Have you ever watched the musical "The Sound of Music" on television? It is really a very romantic story – but did you know that it is based on the lives of real people? Maria wrote a book about her family's eventful life, and it was later adapted into a popular Broadway musical by Rodgers and Hammerstein. Later, her story went on to become one of the most-watched motion pictures ever, starring Julie Andrews and the Canadian actor Christopher Plummer. Although the film was made more than 40 years ago, it is still as popular as ever.

Maria Augusta Kutschera was born in Austria on January 26, 1905. During World War One, while Captain Georg von Trapp commanded an Austrian submarine and was becoming a decorated soldier, Maria was a student. After World War One, Captain von Trapp married a woman named Agathe Whitehead and became a businessman. After having seven children together, his wife died of scarlet fever. The captain realized he needed someone to help him raise his seven unruly children, and engaged a young woman studying at a nearby Benedictine nunnery – Maria. Eventually the captain and Maria married, and had three more children together. The family formed a musical group, the Trapp Family Singers. In reality, Captain von Trapp's business fortune had been lost in the Depression, and so the family was singing in order to earn a living. The group became famous and sang all over Europe.

In 1938, when Hitler annexed Austria, the family fled the country by hiking over the mountains to Switzerland. They eventually emigrated to the United States and settled in Vermont. They continued to sing and became famous once again, this time to the delight of audiences in North America. In 1950, the family opened a small ski lodge in Vermont, inspired by their life in the mountains of Salzburg, Austria. In 1983, it was expanded from 27 to 93 rooms.

The property includes 2700 acres of cross-country skiing and hiking trails, facilities for tennis, croquet, snowshoeing, sleighrides, maple sugaring, and of course, music lessons. The Trapp Family Lodge is one of Vermont's most popular tourist attractions.

Captain von Trapp died in 1947, but Maria lived until 1987, dying of cancer at the age of 82. The Trapp Family Lodge is now managed by Georg and Maria's son Johannes. Several of Maria and Captain von Trapp's grandchildren and great-grandchildren are accomplished musicians and singers in their own right.

A. Choose and underline the main idea of each of the paragraphs in the passage.

Paragraph One

A. "The Sound of Music" is a musical based on the lives of Maria and her family.

B. Although "The Sound of Music" was made more than 40 years ago, it is as popular as ever.

C. Christopher Plummer and Julie Andrews starred in the movie "The Sound of Music".

Paragraph Two

A. Captain von Trapp's wife died of scarlet fever and so he married Maria.

B. Captain von Trapp married Maria, who took care of his seven children and formed a family musical group.

C. Captain von Trapp became a businessman after World War One but he lost his fortune in the Depression.

Paragraph Three

A. The family fled Austria in 1938 and became famous in North America.

B. Inspired by their life in Salzburg, Austria, the von Trapp family operated a family lodge in Vermont.

C. The family fled the Nazis and settled in Vermont where they continued to sing and operate the Trapp Family Lodge.

Paragraph Four

A. Captain von Trapp died in 1947 and Maria died in 1987.

B. Georg and Maria's legacy continued through some of their descendents who were accomplished musicians and singers.

C. Georg and Maria had many grandchildren and great-grandchildren.

B. **Imagine you are Maria's friend. Write why you convinced her to write about her family.**

"Maria never intended to write anything of her life, but a friend persistently pleaded with her not to allow her story to be forgotten by others. She denied she had any writing skill whatsoever, but her friend was not to be put off and kept on asking her whenever they saw each other. Finally, one day, in desperation, Maria excused herself and went to her room for an hour to scribble a few pages about her life story, hoping to prove once and for all she was no writer. However, this displayed such natural writing talent that she reluctantly agreed to finish what she had started, and her jottings formed the basis of the first chapter of her memoirs. Her book, The Story of the Trapp Family Singers, was a best-seller."

– Excerpted from Wikipedia

The reason I was always pleading and trying to convince Maria, to write about her life was because, she thought that she did not have any writings skill so I wanted to help her believe that she did. And because I though that she was special and that she could do amazing things if she tried. And that I saw potential in her that she would be great and famous and that her life story is amazing.

didn't

Active Voice and Passive Voice

In sentences written in the active voice, the subject performs the action expressed in the verb.

Example: Maria wrote the book "The Story of the Trapp Family Singers".

In sentences written in the passive voice, the subject receives the action expressed in the verb.

Example: The book "The Story of the Trapp Family Singers" was written by Maria.

C. Change the following sentences from the active voice to the passive voice or the other way round.

1. Captain Georg von Trapp commanded an Austrian submarine during World War One.

    The austrian submarine was commaned by capun George von trapp during world war one.

2. The story was later adapted into a popular Broadway musical by Rodgers and Hammerstein.

    rodgers and Hammerstein adapted the story into a poupuler Broadway musical.

3. The family formed a musical group, the Trapp Family Singers.

    a musical group was formel by the trapp family singers.

4. In 1950, the von Trapp family opened a small ski lodge in Vermont.

    the von trapp family opened a small ski lodge in Vermont in 1950.

5. The Trapp Family Lodge is now managed by Georg and Maria's son Johannes.

    Georg and Maria's son Johannes mange the trapp family lodge.

6. Maria's friend convinced her to write about her life.

    Maria was convinced by her friend to write about her life.

A History of Avian Flu

Throughout history, epidemics and pandemics have posed a threat to human society. One of the most well-known scourges of all time has been the Bubonic Plague – the "Black Death" – which ravaged Europe and parts of the Middle East and Asia during the Middle Ages. It is estimated that this rodent-borne plague killed one-third of the population of Europe.

Since the beginning of the 20th century, however, the flu has been our greatest cause for concern. The largest pandemic of all time is the 1918 "Spanish Flu" (so-called because this flu, spread worldwide by soldiers returning home after World War One, was most widely reported in Spain, which was not involved in the war and where newspapers were not subject to wartime censorship). This pandemic killed over 40 million people in one and a half years, 5% of the world's population. Mortality rates were high in areas all around the world, from Alaska to France to India. Recently, studies were carried out on the bodies of World War One soldiers and an Inuit woman, which had been preserved in the Alaskan permafrost. Examination confirmed that they had been infected with the H1N1 virus – a virus stemming from birds.

More avian flu outbreaks occurred later in the century. The 1957 "Asian Flu", caused by the H2N2 influenza virus, claimed over 100 000 lives, and in 1968, the "Hong Kong Flu" pandemic, caused by the H3N2 virus, resulted in more than 700 000 deaths. Hong Kong was also in the news in 1997 when the avian flu virus H5N1 began infecting people there, eventually claiming six lives. The same virus killed another person in Hong Kong the following year.

Viruses are always mutating, making it difficult for human bodies to develop immunity to them – and this is one of the reasons why viral illnesses can sometimes be so contagious. In 2003, another strain of the virus, H7N7, infected 83 people, resulting in one death. In 2004, the H5N1 and H7N3 strains caused deaths in Vietnam and Thailand, as well as two cases of infection in Canada. Now, more viral strains are being detected in birds as far away as Romania, Greece, Turkey, and Russia. Epidemiologists are afraid that the next time such a virus mutates, it could pass from human to human. If this form of transmission occurs, another big pandemic could result.

But there is good news. Everyone is aware of the situation, and disease-control centres throughout the world are making avian flu their top priority. In the meantime, you can help protect yourself by staying away from wild birds, and washing your hands thoroughly when handling raw and cooked poultry.

A. Underline the best answer for each of the following questions.

1. Which one of these statements is correct?

    A. The Bubonic Plague killed a third of the people in the Middle East and Asia.

    B. The Black Death was caused by rodents.

    C. The Bubonic Plague spared only a third of the population in Europe.

2. The Spanish Flu pandemic _____ .

    A. was caused by the first world war

    B. affected 5% of the world's population

    C. spread worldwide after the first world war

3. Which of these statements is NOT true?

    A. The Spanish Flu is the largest pandemic of all time.

    B. Some bodies of the World War One soldiers were preserved in Alaska for future examination.

    C. Spain was not one of the warring countries during the first world war.

4. Mutating viruses _____ .

    A. leave no traces for doctors to follow and cure the disease

    B. make it difficult for our bodies to develop immunity to them

    C. make it difficult for scientists to identify them

5. The most fatal pandemic mentioned in the passage is _____ .

    A. the Black Death

    B. the Spanish Flu

    C. the Hong Kong Flu

19

B. Based on the passage, list the most significant event that occurred in each of the following periods of time.

Period of Time	Event
The Middle Ages	The black death
1918	The Spanish flu
1957	the Asian flu.
1968	The Hong kong flu
1997	The avian flu
1998	H5N1
2003	H7N7
2004	H5N1 and H7N3

Do you think another big pandemic would break out soon? Why or why not?

I think that another big pandemic would break out. because as the animal population increase rapidly more diases will emerge and more panderics.

C. Read the following definitions and find the appropriate words in the passage. Write them on the lines provided.

1. attacked and damaged
    _____

2. without being affected
    _____

3. not allowing the reporting of certain news or information
    _____

4. the number of people who die
    _____

5. land permanently frozen to a great depth
    _____

6. developing different characteristics as a result of changes in genes
    _____

7. types
    _____

8. scientists researching epidemics
    _____

9. easily passed from one person to another
    _____

10. chickens, ducks, and other birds kept for their eggs and meat
    _____

11. something likely to cause danger
    _____

12. things that cause suffering
    _____

D. Use your dictionary to find the definitions of these words with similar meanings.

1. epidemics _____
    _____

2. pandemics _____
    _____

3. plague _____
    _____

4. outbreaks _____
    _____

The World's Most Unusual Animals

You know about those weird egg-laying mammals from Australia: the duck-billed platypus and the shiny echidna. You've probably heard of the annual migration of the gnu – or wildebeest. You've seen photos of New Zealand's flightless bird, the kiwi, and you know why we have given that name to a particular round, brown-green fuzzy fruit (otherwise known as the Chinese gooseberry). You've heard about the assortment of elegant antelope species that roam Africa: gazelle, springbok – and maybe even the kudu, eland, and dik-dik. But still, there are so many animals left to discover. Have you ever heard of these?

The **capybara** is the world's largest rodent that lives in the rainforests of South America. It likes to live near the water; its partially-webbed feet and hippo-like body are well-adapted for this habitat. A full-grown male is 135 centimetres long and can weigh as much as 65 kilograms. They look like overgrown guinea pigs!

The **jerboa** is a small African rodent with legs so powerful that it can jump up to 10 feet in one leap. It is especially unusual because it never drinks. Instead, it gets its moisture from the insects it eats.

The **okapi** is what an animal would look like if a horse mated with a zebra. But this African animal is actually a relative of the giraffe! It looks like a reddish-brown horse, with white stripes on its rump and hind legs.

The **tomato frog** is found only in Madagascar. It is a bright reddish-orange colour. When threatened, the tomato frog inflates itself into what looks like a big, ripe, red tomato! By appearing larger than it actually is, predators may be scared away, and so this kind of puffery is actually a form of self-defence.

The **guanaco** is one of a group of camel-like animals that live in South America. Its soft undercoat is even more prized than that of its cousins, the llama, alpaca, and vicuna. The colour can vary from a light to dark reddish-brown. Guanacos are cute-looking animals, with large doe-like brown eyes, and streamlined and energetic bodies.

The **long-nosed chimaera** is an ancient deep-sea relative of sharks and stingrays, but it looks like a slimy sea creature, with a serpent's tail, a shark-like body, and a pointy duckbill! The chimaera was the subject of Greek legend – said to be of lion, goat, and serpent. It lives mainly in the ocean depths of the southern hemisphere.

A. State the most distinctive feature that makes the following animals so unusual.

Animal	Most Distinctive Feature
1. The capybara	
2. The jerboa	
3. The okapi	
4. The tomato frog	
5. The guanaco	
6. The long-nosed chimaera	

Your View

Which among all the animals mentioned in the passage do you think is the most unusual? Explain why you think so.

_____

_____

_____

_____

_____

5

B. Read the clues and complete the following crossword puzzles.

Noun Form

Clues:

A. slimy

B. deep

C. discover

1. moist

Root Word

Clues:

A. hemisphere

1. puffery

2. energetic

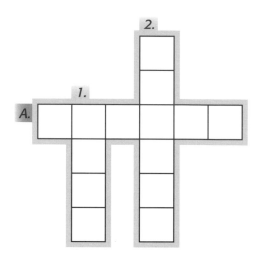

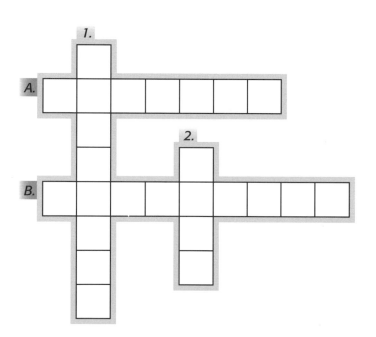

Opposite

Clues:

A. modern

B. entirely

1. deflates

2. fore

C. Find five compound words from the passage. Write them in the space below.

Compound Word

24

D. Read the example below and describe the following animals in a similar way.

species ⟶

⟵ habitat

special features ⟶

⟵ size

in comparison with ⟶
another animal

The capybara is the world's largest rodent that lives in the rainforests of South America. It likes to live near the water; its partially-webbed feet and hippo-like body are well-adapted for this habitat. A full-grown male is 135 centimetres long and can weigh as much as 65 kilograms. They look like overgrown guinea pigs!

1. The raccoon _____

_____

_____

_____

_____

_____

_____

2. The beaver _____

_____

_____

_____

_____

_____

_____

3. The moose _____

_____

_____

_____

_____

_____

Extreme Road-tripping: the Pan-American Highway

Did you know you can drive a car from Fairbanks, Alaska, all the way to Quellón, Chile, at the tip of South America via the Pan-American Highway? Well, *almost*...although you had better think of using a four-wheel drive vehicle. And don't let the word "highway" fool you; the Pan-American Highway is not a paved, four-lane thoroughfare, but one of the most difficult and extreme road trips in the world!

Actually, the Pan-American Highway is a network of routes linking North and South America through Central America. It is almost 48 000 kilometres in length and joins the following countries: Canada, the United States, Mexico, Guatemala, El Salvador, Honduras, Nicaragua, Costa Rica, Panama, Venezuela, Colombia, Ecuador, Peru, Chile, and Argentina. From Venezuela, the Trans-Amazonian Highway links to Brazil.

So, where does the *almost* come in? There is a place where no highway exists – do you know where it is? Maybe you are thinking that drivers need to take their vehicles on ferries to cross the Panama Canal. In fact, while the Panama Canal was under American jurisdiction (from 1904, upon commencement of construction, to December 31, 1999, when the transfer of canal operations to Panama was completed), a high-level bridge was built over it.

The mysterious gap in the Pan-American Highway is a stretch of rainforest and swampland 87 km long. Fittingly, it is called the Darién Gap. It lies just south of the Panama Canal in Central America, and ends at the border to Colombia, part of the South American mainland. The Colombian side of the Darién Gap is the extensive flat swampland of the Atrato River Delta. In contrast, the Panamanian side is dominated by steep, forested valleys and mountainous terrain.

Over the years, intrepid travellers have traversed the Darién Gap by all-terrain vehicle, motorcycle, Range Rover, and on foot. And for decades, there have been concerted efforts to close this one last, tiny gap in the vast Pan-American Highway system. But the cost of building a permanent road through the area, and the opposition to the environmental impact such

construction would involve – have so far made the project untenable. Studies have shown that the Darién Gap has provided a natural barrier to the spread of disease, primarily in livestock, and has helped provide stability for the indigenous peoples of the area, and the continuation of their tribal cultures.

It seems inevitable that, someday, a way will be found to "bridge the Darién Gap", so to speak. But, the real question is: *Should we?*

A. Answer these questions.

1. Why did the writer suggest using a four-wheel drive vehicle on the Pan-American Highway?

   _____

   _____

2. Which country had the operation rights of the Panama Canal when it was first built?

   _____

3. Briefly describe the Darién Gap.

   _____

   _____

4. Give one reason mentioned in the passage why the Darién Gap should not be bridged.

   _____

Do you think the Pan-American Highway should be developed into a full-fledged highway? Why or why not?

_____

_____

_____

_____

B. Circle the words in the word search.

Synonym of
- fearless
- crossed
- beginning
- vast

Antonym of
- temporary
- individual

Compound word meaning
- main road

Derivative of
- stable

e	x	t	n	i	e	x	t	e	n	s	i	v	e	j	b	k	i	s
p	e	r	m	o	u	e	h	n	f	p	n	x	g	m	c	s	n	j
o	r	a	c	t	e	p	o	s	i	v	t	p	a	o	o	t	t	r
c	t	h	o	r	o	u	g	h	f	a	r	e	p	c	m	a	r	g
k	l	x	n	a	v	m	r	u	d	p	e	r	n	a	m	b	o	u
m	f	n	c	v	c	v	o	v	g	e	p	m	i	l	o	i	p	i
c	o	n	c	e	r	t	e	d	w	a	i	a	o	d	e	l	p	o
l	b	y	e	r	g	t	h	q	e	j	d	n	g	r	c	i	i	s
d	r	h	k	s	c	o	m	m	e	n	c	e	m	e	n	t	d	t
n	e	x	t	e	n	i	s	e	v	k	t	n	s	e	j	y	e	a
i	d	l	e	d	i	b	m	c	o	a	s	t	a	b	l	i	t	y

C. Complete the following sentences with words from the passage.

1. The Pan-American Highway ＿＿＿＿＿＿ up many countries in North, Central, and South America.

2. On the Colombian side of the Darién Gap is a large piece of ＿＿＿＿＿＿ .

3. The mountainous ＿＿＿＿＿＿ makes travelling treacherous.

4. The ＿＿＿＿＿＿ of the Panama Canal started in 1904.

5. The Panama Canal is now under Panama's ＿＿＿＿＿＿ .

6. Closing the Darién Gap will lead to many ＿＿＿＿＿＿ concerns.

7. The Darién Gap actually helps preserve ＿＿＿＿＿＿ cultures.

D. Imagine you have a pen pal in Brazil. Write an e-mail to him/her explaining how you can actually travel from Canada to Brazil by taking the Pan-American Highway. Stress the exciting side of such a road trip.

WEIRD
Teen Trends

Do you think one of the most important things to a teenager is to be trendy? How important is it to be a part of what other people think is hip or cool? The thing is, what is fashionable and all the rage one week can be very out of style the next. It takes a lot of effort to stay on top of the current trends. Sometimes, too, these trends can be silly or downright dangerous. Take a look at the following two teen trends and decide for yourself.

Recently in Thailand, it was a big fad among young people, especially teenaged girls, to wear fake orthodontic braces. Soon shops everywhere in Thailand, from the cities' shopping malls to small village stores, were stocking fake braces in an assortment of bright colours. These bits of metal were sold in do-it-yourself kits, along with glue. The trendy teens would glue these bits onto their teeth, or some would take them to people who claimed they were dentists and orthodontists, and who were happy to put the fake braces on, for a fee.

Soon, legitimate doctors, dentists, and orthodontists began to decry the trend. Studies carried out on some of these fake decorative braces showed they were made of lead and other harmful materials, and the glue was toxic. There were cases of girls choking on, and swallowing, metal bits that came off. The government declared it an offence to manufacture or sell the fake braces, and the fad quickly died down.

In China, trend-conscious teenagers were in buying up collections of cute dolls. Of course, the popularity of cute dolls or the newest game is nothing new – but these dolls were marketed as "voodoo dolls". Voodoo is an ancient system of religious beliefs and practices, originating in Africa. But voodoo dolls, as we know them today, are considered by some to be a means by which we can inflict harm on others.

Soon, voodoo dolls were being brought to schools in China, and students were using them to, among other things, wish bad luck on their fellow students during exam time. All this voodoo doll activity was disrupting school life. Again, the government stepped in and banned the sale of these voodoo dolls, and school staff was given the authority to confiscate them.

Was it worth it to be "trendy" for a little while? How important is it to get the newest "must-haves"? Are you a follower, or do you lead your own life?

A. Read each of the following sentences. Write what happened as a result.

1. Teenaged girls in Thailand liked wearing fake orthodontic braces.

   _____

   _____

2. Studies carried out on some of these fake decorative braces showed they were made of lead and other harmful materials, and the glue was toxic.

   _____

   _____

3. All this voodoo doll activity was disrupting school life.

   _____

   _____

Which of these two teen trends is weirder, wearing fake orthodontic braces or collecting voodoo dolls? Explain why you think so.

_____

_____

_____

_____

_____

B. Read the clues and complete the crossword puzzle with words from the passage.

Across

A. criticize strongly

B. officially forbidden

C. dental

D. seize

E. strange, odd

F. preventing something from continuing

Down

1. variety

2. positively

3. something that is very popular for a short time

4. very modern

5. something acceptable according to the law

6. make somebody suffer

C. Read the example. Then compose a short paragraph based on each of the following topic sentences.

Recently in Thailand, it was a big fad among young people, especially teenaged girls, to wear fake orthodontic braces.   ← Topic sentence

Soon shops everywhere in Thailand, from the cities' shopping malls to small village stores, were stocking fake braces in an assortment of bright colours.   ← Supporting sentence to illustrate the fad

These bits of metal were sold in do-it-yourself kits, along with glue.   ← Details about the fake braces

The trendy teens would glue these bits onto their teeth, or some would take them to people who claimed they were dentists and orthodontists, and who were happy to put the fake braces on, for a fee.   ← How teens had the fake braces put on their teeth

1. People today are more health-conscious than before. _____

   _____

   _____

   _____

   _____

2. We are planning to stage a variety show on Saturday evening. _____

   _____

   _____

   _____

   _____

3. The weather suddenly turned nasty. _____

   _____

   _____

   _____

Amelia Earhart

Amelia Earhart is perhaps the world's most famous female aviator. Born in Kansas, U.S.A. in 1897, Amelia's childhood was marked by the invention of the airplane. At the age of ten, she saw an airplane for the first time, at the Iowa State Fair. When she took her first short flight at a stunt-flying exhibition at the age of 22, Amelia was hooked! She began taking flying lessons with the female aviation pioneer, Anita Snook, who felt that Amelia showed real promise.

In 1927, the American Charles Lindbergh became the first person to fly solo across the Atlantic Ocean. Months later, Amelia joined a crew of two men in a small Fokker F7 to become the first woman to fly the Atlantic. The flight took 21 hours, and Amelia did take control of the plane for a brief time, and the plane was badly damaged on landing. This did not stop Amelia from becoming an instant hero in the United States, though. In fact, people started calling her "Lady Lindy", a reference to Charles Lindbergh, who was by then known as "Lucky Lindy".

Amelia became more determined than ever to prove herself. She married her manager, George Putnam, who guided her publicity appearances and endorsements that provided the money needed in the expensive world of aviation. Amelia's solo-flying career took off. In 1931 she set a world altitude record of 18 415 feet (5613 metres). In 1932, she became the first woman to solo the Atlantic when she flew from Newfoundland to Northern Ireland (she was supposed to land in Paris). In 1935, she became the first person to solo from Hawaii to the U.S. mainland. She held several transcontinental speed records.

On July 2, 1937, Amelia and her co-pilot Fred Noonan took off from the tiny island of Lae, in Papua New Guinea. They were on their way to Howland Island, heading towards the United States on the world's first aerial circumnavigation of the Earth along the equatorial route. But they never made it to their destination.

The disappearance of Amelia Earhart has been one of recent history's most enduring mysteries. Some say that she was able to land her plane on a small atoll and later died of thirst. Others say she had been working for the United States government, and had been captured by Japanese forces in the Pacific.

One thing is certain, however: Amelia Earhart was a courageous flyer, and an inspiration to generations of aviation enthusiasts, and to girls and women everywhere.

A. Underline the main idea of each paragraph.

Paragraph One

A. Amelia Earhart became interested in flying after her first short flight.

B. Amelia Earhart saw an airplane at the age of ten.

Paragraph Two

A. Amelia Earhart became the first woman to fly across the Atlantic.

B. Charles Lindbergh became known as "Lucky Lindy" while Amelia Earhart was referred to as "Lady Lindy".

Paragraph Three

A. Amelia Earhart's flying career took off.

B. Amelia became the first woman to solo the Atlantic in 1932.

Paragraph Four

A. On July 2, 1937, Amelia had an unsuccessful attempt on the world's first aerial circumnavigation of the Earth along the equatorial route.

B. Amelia wanted to fly from Lae to Howland Island on July 2, 1937.

Paragraph Five

A. Amelia managed to land her plane but later died of thirst.

B. Amelia disappeared mysteriously on her flight along the equatorial route.

B. List the records that Amelia Earhart set.

_____

_____

_____

_____

_____

_____

_____

_____

C. Answer these questions.

1. Explain what Anita Snook probably saw in Amelia that made her feel that Amelia showed real promise.

_____

_____

2. Why was Amelia called "Lady Lindy"?

_____

_____

3. In what way did George Putnam help Amelia?

_____

_____

4. Why do you think Amelia attempted to fly along the equatorial route?

_____

_____

5. How would you describe Amelia Earhart?

_____

_____

D. **Read the clues and complete the crossword puzzle with words from the passage.**

Across

A. first one to do something
B. extremely interested in something
C. travelling around
D. way, path
E. a group of coral islands

Down

1. lasting
2. the height above sea level
3. from one continent to another
4. people interested in a particular activity
5. alone
6. flying aircraft

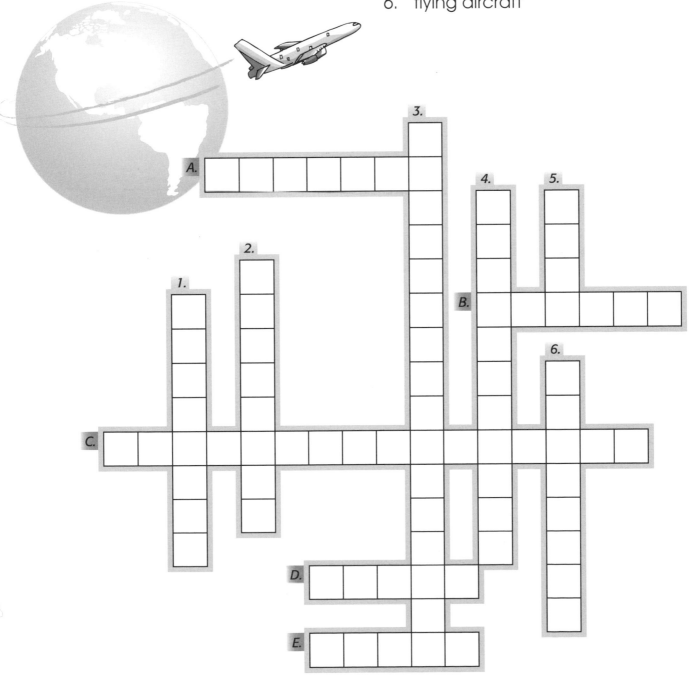

The Ultimate Tourist

It seems that there is no such thing as a "final frontier" anymore. There is nowhere left on this planet to explore, and places that seemed to be far-flung and unreachable only a few decades ago are now accessible within 24 hours. It seems that everyone has seen the world, whether in real life or on TV. Everyone is a tourist now – even an armchair tourist. Is there nowhere new to go?

Well, perhaps there is. Space tourism is a recent phenomenon. After the establishment of NASA's space shuttle program in 1977, and with construction commencing on the International Space Station in 1998, it seemed inevitable that, someday, outer space would become accessible to the general public. We began dreaming of a world where regular people, instead of hopping on a flight across the Atlantic, would hop on a shuttle, and orbit the Earth – and maybe even make a stopover on the moon!

Well, a part of that futuristic scenario has already become reality. In 2001, an American multi-millionaire, Dennis Tito, became the world's first "space tourist". He paid the Russian government a fee to fly on their Soyuz spacecraft to the International Space Station for a seven-day stay – just as we might buy a package deal to any popular tourist destination for the holidays. South African millionaire Mark Shuttleworth and American scientist and entrepreneur Gregory Olsen were next. They each paid 20 million U.S. dollars for the privilege – with no discounts! Soon other people began expressing interest in becoming a space tourist, including Lance Bass, a rock star with the boy band 'N Sync!

The world's entrepreneurs are taking note; space tourism is a growth industry. British billionaire, Sir Richard Branson, who started Virgin Atlantic and Virgin Blue Airlines, has recently founded Virgin Galactic. His mission is to develop commercial suborbital flights by 2008. Now, several companies around the world are in the race to be the first to offer commercial space flight to "ordinary people" – provided they can afford the ticket.

As exciting as it sounds, commercial space flight has its detractors. Many people are asking why so much time, effort, and money is being spent on space tourism when it could all be better spent dealing with problems such as pollution, hunger, and disease here on Earth. But others say it is humankind's destiny to venture beyond this planet, to see this "big, blue marble" from orbit, to head to Mars – and, maybe, with a stopover on the moon.

A. Answer these questions.

1. What do you think is an armchair tourist?

_____

2. Explain why the writer thinks that "...there is no such thing as a 'final frontier' anymore."

_____

_____

3. What makes outer space travel for ordinary people possible?

_____

_____

4. Describe briefly the first commercial space flight.

_____

_____

Are you in support of commercial space flight? Why or why not?

_____

_____

_____

_____

_____

_____

B. Match the definitions with the following words from the passage. Write the letters.

- **A** critics
- **B** special right or advantage
- **C** the way a situation may develop
- **D** remote
- **E** fate
- **F** can be reached
- **G** something that is observed to happen
- **H** a strong commitment to achieve something
- **I** find out more about something
- **J** those who set up businesses

1. entrepreneurs _____
2. explore _____
3. far-flung _____
4. accessible _____
5. mission _____
6. detractors _____
7. destiny _____
8. phenomenon _____
9. privilege _____
10. scenario _____

C. Write the root words of the following words from the passage.

1. accessible _____
2. futuristic _____
3. suborbital _____
4. tourism _____
5. establishment _____
6. destination _____
7. billionaire _____
8. international _____

D. Imagine you are Sir Richard Branson at a press conference to launch his company, Virgin Galactic. How would you sell your grand plan of space travel for the "ordinary people"? How would you excite the attendees at the press conference? Write your speech in the space provided.

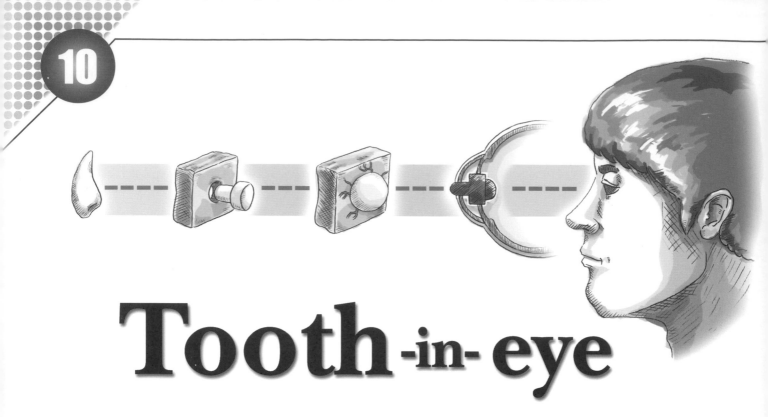

Tooth-in-eye

Our sense of sight is perhaps our most important human sense, and much medical research goes into ways to prevent and cure blindness. It seems that medical breakthroughs are becoming commonplace; but even so, there is one technique that can restore eyesight to some patients that you may find very surprising!

Blindness can occur for many reasons, including accidents and illness, such as diabetes. Another cause of blindness is related to physical problems with parts of the eye. For example, blindness can occur when the cornea becomes damaged. The cornea is the clear, dome-shaped covering over the pupil and iris. It helps to refract the light, allowing us to see. In the past, the standard procedure for attempting to restore eyesight to a patient with a damaged cornea was to transplant a healthy cornea from a cadaver!

Transplantation has side-effects. When any organ or body part given by a donor is transplanted into the recipient, there is a chance that it will be rejected. Because of this, medical researchers are always trying to devise ways of having the recipient's own body be involved in the manufacture of "spare parts". This concept has been used in a new kind of corneal transplantation. A new cornea is created...in the patient's own mouth – using a tooth! It is called the "tooth-in-eye" technique.

Actually, this "tooth-in-eye" procedure was first developed in the 1960s in Italy, but was not very successful. Recent advances in surgical techniques, however, made the procedure more successful and now it is performed by top ocular surgeons around the world.

The surgery is complex, and involves two stages. First, the damaged eye is cleared of scar tissue. Then doctors take one of the patient's canine teeth, as well as some adjacent bone and jaw ligaments. These are shaped, and a hole is drilled into the tooth and bone to allow for a tiny plastic corneal device to be implanted. This amalgam of human tooth, bone, and tissue, and artificial plastic "cornea" is called an "optical cylinder". The optical cylinder is then implanted into the patient's cheek for several months. During this time, human tissue grows over it.

In the second stage, an opening is made in the patient's damaged eye. The optical cylinder, which is now a piece of living human tissue, is removed from the cheek and implanted into the eyeball. Light enters the optical cylinder which refracts the light like a cornea, thereby restoring vision to the patient. The success rate is high – around 80 to 90%, and doctors believe that vision can be restored for up to 50 years.

A. Choose and underline the correct answers.

1. The standard procedure for restoring vision is to replace the damaged _____ with a healthy one.

   A. iris   B. cornea   C. pupil

2. Rejection is more likely when a _____ cornea is transplanted.

   A. plastic   B. donated   C. damaged

3. The optical cylinder is _____ into the patient's cheek for tissue to grow over it.

   A. transplanted   B. implanted   C. transposed

4. Which of the following statements is true?

   A. The "tooth-in-eye" procedure was first developed in Italy.

   B. The "tooth-in-eye" technique is still being tried out around the world.

   C. Worldwide use of the "tooth-in-eye" technique began in 1960.

5. An optical cylinder comprises _____ .

   A. a tooth, some bone and ligaments, and a donated cornea

   B. a plastic cornea, a tooth, and some ligaments

   C. some bone and ligaments, a tooth, and a plastic cornea

6. Which of the following statements is NOT true?

   A. The "tooth-in-eye" procedure can restore 90% of the patient's vision.

   B. The "tooth-in-eye" procedure involves two stages.

   C. The "tooth-in-eye" procedure takes several months to complete.

B. Write the adjective form of the following words from the passage.

1. procedure _____

2. organ _____

3. prevent _____

4. concept _____

5. sense _____

6. cure _____

C. Write the noun form of the following words from the passage.

1. restore _____

2. grows _____

3. involves _____

4. occur _____

5. believe _____

6. refract _____

7. performed _____

8. removed _____

9. enters _____

10. clear _____

D. Find the compound words used in the passage and write them in the space below.

━━━━━━━━ **Compound Word** ━━━━━━━━

E. Explain the meanings of the prefixes "trans" and "im" as used with "plant".

1. transplant: _____

   _____

2. implant: _____

   _____

F. Imagine you are an ocular surgeon. Explain to your patient why the "tooth-in-eye" procedure is better than the standard transplant and how the procedure is carried out.

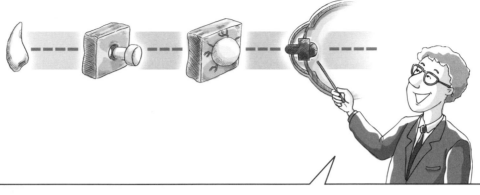

_____

_____

_____

_____

_____

_____

_____

_____

_____

_____

_____

_____

_____

_____

_____

He Climbed
Mount Everest

On May 15, 2006, a New Zealand man made a historic "first" at the top of Mt. Everest. No, it wasn't Sir Edmund Hillary, the beekeeper from Christchurch who became world-famous in 1953 when he successfully reached the summit of the world's tallest mountain.

Forty-seven-year-old Mark Inglis grew up in the mountainous South Island of New Zealand, and he said that Sir Edmund was an inspiration to him. Mark started climbing at a young age, and by the age of 20 was a professional climber, working as a search-and-rescue mountaineer in Aoraki/Mt. Cook National Park. So what made his ascent of Everest a "first"? Mark Inglis is a double amputee. He is the first person to climb Mt. Everest with two artificial legs.

How did Mark lose his legs? In 1982, Mark and his climbing partner were climbing Mt. Cook, New Zealand's highest peak, when a fierce blizzard engulfed the mountain. The two climbers were trapped in an ice cave for 14 days. They suffered severe frostbite, and both Mark's legs had to be amputated below the knee.

But this did not stop Mark from doing what he loved. He was fitted with prosthetic legs and began climbing again. In 2002, Mark successfully reached the summit of Mt. Cook. In 2004, he conquered Cho Oyu, the world's sixth-highest mountain. Mark knew he had to try to climb Everest. His ascent of Everest took 40 days. At about 6400 metres, one of his special carbon-fibre prosthetic legs snapped, and was repaired with duct tape while a spare leg was brought up the mountain. He suffered from laryngitis and also frostbite of the fingers. But none of this prevented Mark from climbing Mt. Everest.

In the days following Mark's success, it emerged that his team had passed by a stricken climber high on the mountain. Each year, there are many deaths on the world's highest peaks; the fact that there are many climbers on the mountain is sometimes the cause. Bottlenecks can occur because climbers from several teams attempt their ascent at the same time during the small window of opportunity provided by weather conditions.

Even Sir Edmund Hillary weighed in with his opinion. He declared that he would have abandoned his ascent in order to help that climber down the mountain. Other mountaineers disagreed, saying that experienced climbers understand the dangers and accept the notion that, at such heights, it is difficult enough to keep oneself alive. Sadly, that fallen climber later died.

A. Answer these questions.

1. What is a double amputee?

   _____

2. Why do you think scaling Mt. Everest is so dangerous?

   _____

3. What happened to Mark Inglis that might have foiled his plan of reaching the summit of Mt. Everest?

   _____

4. What does "the small window of opportunity" suggest?

   _____

B. Imagine you are Mark Inglis. Give an account of what happened when you were climbing Mount Cook in 1982.

_____

_____

_____

_____

_____

_____

_____

_____

C. Read the clues and complete the crossword puzzle with words from the passage.

Across

A. upward journey
B. cut off
C. trapped; in danger
D. opposite of amateur
E. not natural; man-made
F. covered completely

Down

1. snowstorm with strong winds
2. top
3. someone or something that causes people to want to achieve something
4. broke
5. infection of the throat
6. given up

D. Rephrase the following sentences.

1. Mark started climbing at a young age, and by the age of 20 was a professional climber, working as a search-and-rescue mountaineer in Aoraki/ Mt. Cook National Park. He was the first person to climb Mt. Everest with two artificial legs.

   Mark said, " _____

   _____

   _____

   _____ "

2. Even Sir Edmund Hillary weighed in with his opinion. He declared that he would have abandoned his ascent in order to help that climber down the mountain.

   Sir Edmund Hillary said, " _____

   _____

   _____

   _____ "

E. Imagine you are a reporter of your school newspaper and you had a chance to interview Mark Inglis. Think of six questions that you would like to ask him. List your questions on the lines below.

1. _____

   _____

2. _____

3. _____

4. _____

5. _____

6. _____

Ikebana
The Peaceful Power of Flowers

Flowers can do much to bring peace and tranquility to our stressful lives. They can brighten a room, and one's mood, by their bursts of colour. Moreover, potted plants act as nature's air purifiers, taking in the carbon dioxide we breathe out – in addition to other toxins and pollutants found in stale indoor air – and giving back life-sustaining oxygen. Flower arranging is becoming an increasingly popular pastime among people who believe in the idea that one's home is their haven.

Ikebana is the Japanese art of flower arranging. Ikebana – meaning "giving life to flowers" – is an ancient art that was first developed by Buddhist priests in Japan, not long after Buddhism was introduced from China around the sixth century and began influencing Japanese arts and culture. Today Ikebana is popular among men and women of all ages and walks of life in Japan. As with many ancient arts, different schools emerged over time. The most popular are the classic Ikenobo school, with a strict set of rules and geometric sense of space; the Ohara school (an offshoot of Ikenobo) which makes use of the shorter-stemmed flower types that were imported once Japan opened its doors to the West; and Sogetsu, the newest form, which is more free-styling in terms of colour, materials, and space.

Ikebana is founded on the idea of the essential bond between human beings and nature. As an art, Ikebana attempts to recreate the beauty of outdoor landscapes and bring it indoors. The creative use of various types of plant life and flowers, as well as the receptacles in which they are placed, is a way of reducing the scale of nature in its many forms – rivers, lakes, gardens, and valleys. Thus, in an Ikebana arrangement, a vase fashioned from a bamboo frond is a grove; a single peony is a garden. The act of growing and picking flowers – even choosing them at a flower shop – becomes an integral part of the art, in much the same way as every turn of the teacup is a part of the Japanese tea ceremony.

Ikebana is not just about putting flowers in a vase. It is a spiritual endeavour. The act of making an arrangement, and of focusing on an activity, can provide a sense of calm. Communicating with the flowers, and expressing oneself with the beauty of the flowers and nature, can give great peace of mind. It is clear that the study of Ikebana provides plenty of scope for immersing one's self into a satisfying pastime. Those who are keen students of this art will tell you: there is so much to learn from Ikebana – it is a way of living.

A. Answer these questions.

1. What, according to the writer, causes flower arranging to become more and more popular?

   _____

   _____

2. How did Ikebana come about?

   _____

   _____

3. Explain briefly the three schools of Ikebana.

   a. classic Ikenobo: _____

   b. Ohara: _____

   c. Sogetsu: _____

4. Explain how Ikebana helps establish the bond between human beings and nature.

   _____

   _____

5. "It is clear that the study of Ikebana provides plenty of scope for immersing one's self into a satisfying pastime." Explain why this is so.

   _____

   _____

B. **Read the clues and complete the crossword puzzle with words from the passage.**

Across

A. totally involving

B. a group of trees grown closely together

C. something developed from something else

D. essential, fundamental

E. a long leaf with an edge divided into many thin parts

Down

1. two things joining together in some way

2. based on

3. containers

4. relating to thoughts and beliefs

5. giving life to flowers

6. came into existence

7. a sense of calm and serenity

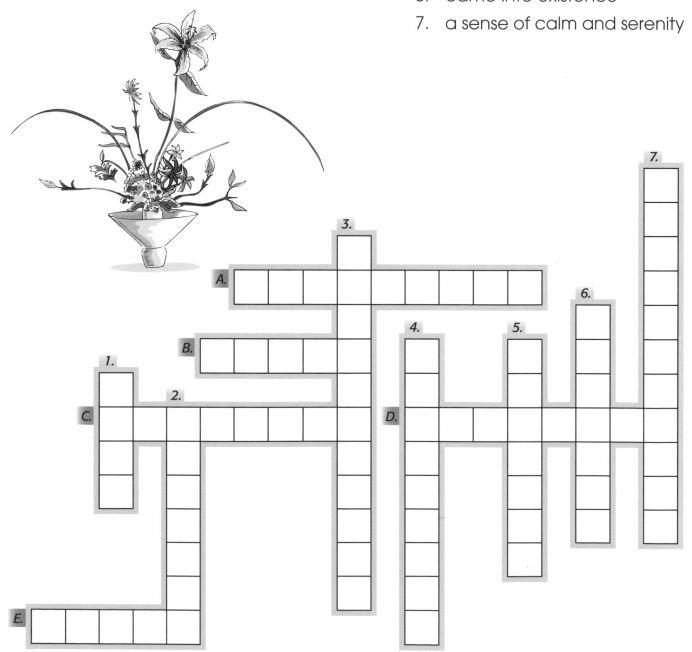

Dashes and Parentheses

We can make use of **dashes** and **parentheses** to include more information in a sentence. By doing so, we can leave out the additional information without affecting the structure of the sentence.

Example: *The act of growing and picking flowers – <u>even choosing them at a flower shop</u> – becomes an integral part of Ikebana.*

The act of growing and picking flowers becomes an integral part of Ikebana.

C. Rewrite the following sentences, adding in the information provided.

1. Flower arranging helps turn one's home into a haven.
   (or Ikebana in Japanese)

   _____

   _____

   _____

2. The act of arranging flowers offers us a sense of calm.
   (and of focusing on an activity)

   _____

   _____

   _____

3. Ikebana attempts to recreate the beauty of outdoor landscapes and bring it indoors.
   (rivers, lakes, gardens, and valleys)

   _____

   _____

   _____

4. Ikebana is an ancient art that was first developed by Buddhist priests in Japan.
   (probably as early as the sixth century)

   _____

   _____

   _____

So You Want to Be an Author

Famous writers are always approached at book-signings by fans wanting hints on how to get published. Some authors (almost always little-known ones) even offer courses on the subject. So-called "agents" will ask for payment to try to get your manuscript sold, but may simply photocopy and mail the work out to publishers, something you could do yourself – and which rarely works, anyway.

But it is not all bad news. If you work at the craft of writing, there is no reason why you, too, cannot have a book in print and sell out the print run. Most writers will tell you that you don't get rich being a published author, but the average person who did manage to get their labour-of-love published will tell you that money was not the motivating factor. It was the chance to see their work in print, and made accessible to those who may share similar interests.

With the advent of desktop publishing and the Internet, becoming published is now much more accessible than before. One intriguing new development is "print-on-demand" (POD) publishing, whereby the author pays the costs of design, as well as a fee to the POD company. The book is then produced, using special machines, only if and when it is ordered, thus eliminating the overhead costs associated with warehousing and distribution. The end product may only be a few dollars more expensive than a book published the traditional way (bookstores can also order a POD book). POD books are especially suitable for subject matter that is narrow in scope – such as local histories or family memoirs – but which may still have enough local interest to generate around 2000 purchases (an average first print run).

Any writer who thinks that having their books on bookstore shelves is the end objective obviously doesn't care if their work is being read. These days, the challenge in becoming an author is not necessarily in securing a publisher, but in being able to sell the book once it is made, and to develop creative marketing and distribution channels. Fewer books are being sold in brick-and-mortar bookshops, no matter how hard these shops try to lure customers with coffee and plush furniture. A Website and promotional appearances are mandatory. The author needs to promote, and this means establishing relationships with all sorts of organizations.

Whether you write for the fun of it, or want to pass down a story to family and friends before it's too late, or think you've got something that will make you the next Harry Potter phenomenon – you, too, can be an author. Just don't give up your day job.

A. Answer these questions.

1. What does the writer think about the function of a book agent?

_____

_____

2. Explain what "print-on-demand" is all about.

_____

_____

3. What does the writer think is important in ensuring that your book sells?

_____

_____

4. Why do you think the writer advises budding writers not to give up their day jobs?

_____

_____

Do you agree with the writer that Web-bookstores have taken a fair share of the book business? Why do you think so?

_____

_____

_____

_____

B. **Read the clues and complete the crossword puzzle with words from the passage.**

Across

A. written account of people and events

B. easy to reach

C. getting rid of

D. interesting

E. people who act on behalf of others

F. skill

Down

1. storing of goods

2. compulsory

3. driving

4. seldom

5. getting hold of

6. something that is observed to happen or exist

C. Read the manuscript below. Correct the misspelled words and the wrong use of punctuation marks and capital letters.

Baseball is a popular sport in north America. It was developed in the United States from an early bat-and-ball game called rounders, and it has became the national sport of the United States, in a game of baseball, the pitcher throws a hard, fist-sized ball pass the hitting area of a batter and the batter tries to hit it with a bat made of wood or metal. A team scores only when batting, by advancing counter clockwise past a series of four bases arranged at the corners of a diamond. Each base is 90 feet from the previous one. Professionel baseball started in the United States in the 1860s when the first fully professional baseball club, the Cincinnati Red Stockings, was formed and went undefeat against a schedule of semi-professional and amature teams, as there were no other fully professional baseball teams that year. The first "major league" was the National association which lasted from 1871 to 1875, the National League was then founded in 1876. Severel other major leagues formed and failed, but the American League, established in 1901 as a major league and origining from the minor Western League (1893), was proofed to be a success. The two leagues began playing a World Series in 1903.

Atlantis
Are You a Believer?

" Now in this island of Atlantis there was a great and wonderful empire which had ruled over the whole island and several others, and over parts of the continent...But afterwards there occurred violent earthquakes and floods, and in a single day and night of misfortune...the island of Atlantis...disappeared in the depths of the sea. "

– Plato, in *Timaeus*

Everyone has heard about one of history's great mysteries: the "lost" civilization of Atlantis. It has been intriguing us since the time of Plato, who wrote about an advanced society of great engineers and architects, whose ancient metropolis on the water was teemed with canals, fountains, and tunnels, with walls encrusted of gems and precious metals.

In the 19th century, speculation about the existence of Atlantis grew when it was theorized that Plato's writings on this lost civilization were in fact a reference to a natural disaster. Volcanic eruptions and tsunamis were not unfamiliar; it was thought that a natural disaster destroyed the Greek island of Rhodes and its legendary Colossus – the huge statue that stood at the harbour, considered to be one of the seven ancient wonders of the world.

It was about this same time that the flourishing Minoan culture, centred on the Greek island of Crete, began its decline, and some theorize that this was also due to a cataclysmic event, perhaps even the same one. Although debated, it is hypothesized that both these events were caused by the eruption of the volcanic island of Santorini around 1500 BCE that destroyed life on the island, and created the spectacular landscape that we see today, with its large watery caldera and rugged cliffs.

The excavations at Akrotiri, at the island's southern end, are of as much interest to believers in Atlantis as to those who come for rest and relaxation. In the dusty steps and lintels, in the pots and shards, we can see for ourselves the proof of ancient life; that people lived here and were going about their business when tragedy struck. Archaeologists say that this was the site of a large and highly-cultured Bronze Age civilization.

The 2004 Boxing Day tsunami has helped us to better understand natural catastrophes of a size we had never before seen but had heard about in legend. It has now become easier to reflect on the final days of ancient peoples – Atlantians, Minoans, and others. In doing so, it seems that a mystery has been revealed to us, in our better understanding of what might have happened on the island of Santorini 3500 years ago. But...was it only Plato's legendary Atlantis?

A. Answer these questions.

1. Why is the lost civilization of Atlantis one of history's great mysteries?

_____

_____

2. What was in common between the two Greek islands: Rhodes and Crete?

_____

_____

3. In what way does the 2004 tsunami make the legend of Atlantis more credible?

_____

_____

4. Summarize in a few sentences what the writer is trying to convey to you through this piece of writing.

_____

_____

Do you think that the island of Santorini was in fact the legendary Atlantis Plato depicted? Support your view with evidence.

_____

_____

_____

_____

_____

B. Look at the compound-complex sentence below and how it can be broken into several shorter sentences. Complete the following exercise in the same way.

"It was about this same time that the flourishing Minoan culture, centred on the Greek island of Crete, began its decline, and some theorize that this was also due to a cataclysmic event, perhaps even the same one."

The shorter sentences:

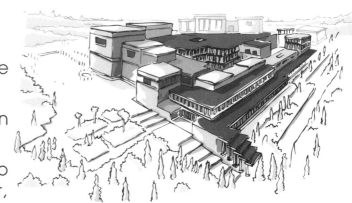

- It was about this same time.
- The flourishing Minoan culture began its decline.
- The Minoan culture was centred on the Greek island of Crete.
- Some theorize that this was also due to a cataclysmic event, perhaps even the same one.

1. It was thought that a natural disaster destroyed the Greek island of Rhodes and its legendary Colossus – the huge statue that stood at the harbour, considered to be one of the seven ancient wonders of the world.

   _____

   _____

   _____

   _____

   _____

2. The excavations at Akrotiri, at the island's southern end, are of as much interest to believers in Atlantis as to those who come for rest and relaxation.

   _____

   _____

   _____

   _____

   _____

C. Read the clues and complete the crossword puzzle with words from the passage.

Across

A. the largest and most important city in a region or a country

B. covered with

C. guess of what might happen

D. people who study societies and peoples of the past

E. arousing one's interest or curiosity

Down

1. impressive, dramatic

2. disastrous

3. assumed

4. something unpleasant and unlucky

5. swarmed

6. people who design buildings

7. prospering, developing successfully

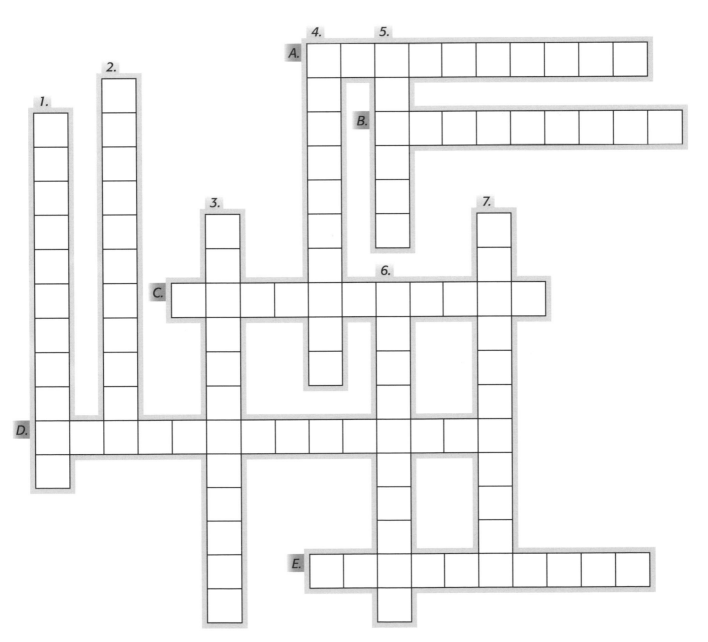

What Is GLOBALIZATION?

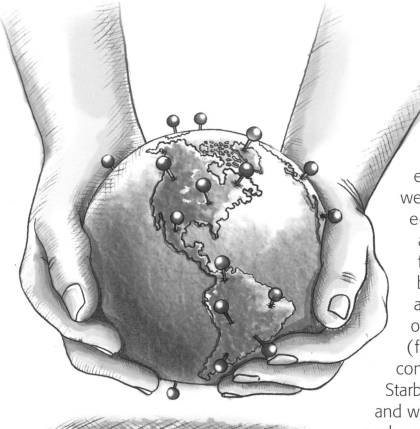

What does globalization mean to you? Globalization means that things that happen in one place in the world have an effect on people in other places as well. It also refers to the spread of economic and cultural activities around the world that originate from, and primarily exist for the benefit of, a particular group, such as the wealthy people who are the owners of the means of production (factories and manufacturing companies). When a Wal-Mart or a Starbucks opens in Manitoba or China, and when Disney opens another theme park somewhere in the world – this is globalization in action.

This is making many people concerned. For example, Disney, Coca-Cola, and McDonalds are three of the world's largest corporations. They have formed an alliance, and have marketed their products successfully around the world. Now, all over the world, children recognize Mickey Mouse; they drink Coke and eat American-style fast food, such as hamburgers and French fries. They believe that globalization is creating a global culture that is mostly American or European, and traditional cultures and values in other parts of the world will be destroyed. Other concerns are that globalization will help the wealthy become wealthier and make the poor become poorer. Wealthy foreign companies will build factories in poor countries, and destroy the environment there. Workers in poorer countries will have to compete against robots used in wealthy countries, and they will earn less money.

Business leaders and political leaders around the world say that globalization will continue, and so these problems must be dealt with. The former Chinese President Jiang Zemin once pointed out that countries that benefit most from free trade and open borders have an obligation to keep the poor countries from falling behind. Li Ka-shing, one of Hong Kong's richest businessmen, has commented that "a new fraternity" to overcome the social problems caused by globalization is needed.

Li said, "For some, success in business is said to come at the price of sacrificing these values [loyalty, integrity, fairness, and compassion]. But it is my belief that the increasing pressures to maximize profit and efficiency should not compromise our respect for equality and our determination to minimize misery." South African president Thabo Mbeki has called for a "new internationalism" based on an understanding that "the problems of poverty and underdevelopment are not the problems only of those who are poor. If they are addressed, they are of benefit also to those who are powerful and wealthy."

A. Write a response to each of the following statements.

1. "Globalization means that things that happen in one place in the world have an effect on people in other places as well." Give an example to illustrate this.

   _____

   _____

   _____

2. "For some, success in business is said to come at the price of sacrificing these values (loyalty, integrity, fairness, and compassion)..." Give an example to show how businesses sometimes sacrifice fairness and compassion for more profits.

   _____

   _____

   _____

3. "...the problems of poverty and underdevelopment are not the problems only of those who are poor. If they are addressed, they are of benefit also to those who are powerful and wealthy." Think of an issue that, if solved, would be a win-win situation for both the poor and the wealthy nations.

   _____

   _____

   _____

B. Read the clues and complete the crossword puzzle with words from the passage.

Across

A. people holding the same interest

B. give in somewhat in order to reach an agreement

C. large businesses

D. beliefs, way of life, and art of a particular people

E. duty

Down

1. a group working towards a similar goal

2. being fair

3. natural surroundings

4. poor and unpleasant living conditions

5. being honest and firm in one's moral principles

Combining Sentences

Sometimes we can improve the flow and organization of our writing by combining simple sentences into compound or complex sentences.

Examples: *Globalization brings people together. It also intensifies inequality.*

Although globalization brings people together, it intensifies inequality.

Disney is now a global brand. Many of its theme parks are located outside the U.S.

Disney is now a global brand and many of its theme parks are located outside the U.S.

C. Combine the following pairs/groups of sentences to form compound or complex sentences.

1. Many people oppose globalization. Many people embrace globalization.

   _____

   _____

2. A Wal-Mart store opens in China. This is globalization in action.

   _____

   _____

3. Some say that globalization benefits only rich people. Rich people control most of the wealth in the world.

   _____

   _____

4. Globalization will continue. The problems as a result of globalization will intensify.

   _____

   _____

5. Globalization benefits the poor too. Job opportunities are now open to the poor. These job opportunities did not exist in the past.

   _____

   _____

The Facts behind the Figures

History can sometimes play with facts. The truth sometimes gets lost in time. Below are some famous historical figures who have well-known reputations. But are these reputations deserved? What do you think?

Count Dracula: National hero – or vampire?

There really was a man named Count Dracula, but he was not a vampire, as many people believe. People think this because of a book called *Dracula*, written by an Englishman named Bram Stoker in 1897. The real Dracula was named Vlad Dracula (Dracula means "son of the dragon") and he lived 500 years ago in what is now Romania. He is considered a national hero there because he helped fight off invading armies. Vlad was not a vampire, but he did like to impale the heads of the soldiers he killed on sticks. Because of this, he is sometimes called Vlad the Impaler, and it is probably this cruel and mean act that inspired Bram Stoker to name his vampire Count Dracula.

The Vandals: Wilful destroyers – or a tribe like any other?

Today, we refer to people who destroy property as "vandals". But this word comes from a tribe of people who lived more than 1500 years ago. The Vandals were just one of several nomadic Germanic tribes (others were Goths, Visigoths, and Franks) in Central Europe at the time. But the Vandal tribe were the best fighters; they captured Rome in 455. The Vandal King Gaiseric ruled harshly.

Johnny Appleseed: Just a storybook character – or a real man?

Many children know the story of Johnny Appleseed, but they may not realize that it is based on John Chapman, who was born in 1774 in Massachusetts. He liked to walk and explore, and did it all his life! He walked for 50 years, as far as what is now the state of Illinois, planting apple seeds wherever he went. He lived alone, spending time with nature and Native American people, whom he got to know well. He became known as the gentle man who liked to plant apple trees, and so his nickname was born! Even today, you can still find some of the old apple trees planted by John Chapman.

Cleopatra: The most beautiful woman in the world?

Cleopatra was the Egyptian queen responsible for uniting the Egyptian and Roman empires. Some people like to say her success was due to her looks; in movies, Cleopatra is always beautiful. But was she really? A few ancient coins, with her face imprinted on them, are kept safe in museums in England and Egypt. The coins show us that Cleopatra had a big neck and sharp features. We don't know how beautiful she was, but we can be sure she was a skilful diplomat. According to the ancient historian Plutarch, Cleopatra had an irresistible charm, and was a good conversationalist. She could also speak several languages. This, of course, made her beauty more than skin deep.

A. State in your own words the facts about the following historical figures.

1. Dracula

   _____

   _____

   _____

2. The Vandals

   _____

   _____

   _____

3. Johnny Appleseed

   _____

   _____

   _____

4. Cleopatra

   _____

   _____

   _____

B. Rewrite the following sentences using the words provided. Make any other necessary changes.

1. There really was a man named Count Dracula, but he was not a vampire.

   Although _____

   _____

2. Dracula is considered a national hero there because he helped fight off invading armies.

   Many people _____

   _____

3. Dracula liked to impale the heads of the soldiers he killed on sticks.

   Impaling _____

   _____

4. We often refer to people who destroy property as "vandals".

   People who _____

   _____

5. The Vandals captured Rome in the year 455.

   Rome _____

   _____

6. The ancient coins show that Cleopatra had a big neck and sharp features.

   Based on _____

   _____

7. Cleopatra was the Egyptian queen responsible for uniting the Egyptian and Roman empires.

   Cleopatra _____ who _____

   _____

C. Read some more facts about Johnny Appleseed. Use descriptive language to write an interesting paragraph about the legendary man.

Johnny Appleseed:

- *a Christian and a businessman*
- *never married; loved chatting with people and playing with children*
- *liked to plant apple trees*
- *often walked barefooted*
- *carried apple seeds and gear on his back*
- *sometimes transported seeds and gear in a boat or canoe*
- *sold his trees for a few pennies each*
- *planted many of the apple trees in the region south of the Great Lakes and between the Ohio and Mississippi Rivers*

_____

_____

_____

_____

_____

_____

_____

_____

_____

_____

_____

_____

Point Pelee
National Park of Canada

A point of land, lush with dense Carolinian forest, extends as far south as northern California. And, like parts of California, it is a part of a grand Monarch butterfly migration flyway, where trees are dense with orange and black in the fall. In spring and fall, people flock from all over to witness the annual bird migrations. If you thought there was no chance this special pocket of land could belong to Canada, you would be mistaken. This prime piece of natural landscape is Point Pelee in Ontario! It has been preserved for us, and for future generations, as Point Pelee National Park of Canada.

The park is only 50 kilometres southeast of Windsor, Ontario, making it the most southerly point on mainland Canada. It is one of our smallest national parks, but attracts almost half a million visitors every year. The fact that the park exists is due to the foresight of some people who, it could be said, were ahead of their time, because they understood the importance of preserving the unique habitat – at a time in Canada's history when so much of our natural resources was being unsustainably exploited. This tiny, green oasis is internationally known for its spring and fall migration of birds and its stunning autumn Monarch butterfly migration. It also offers an unrivalled collection of plants and animals in a wide range of habitats.

Point Pelee was inhabited by Aboriginal peoples for centuries. Because the spit of land was used by European explorers and fur traders as a place to portage their boats, the area became a meeting point of cultures. But it was not always friendly. From about 1760, there are records of several violent skirmishes between natives and Europeans. By 1871, census records show that there was no longer Aboriginal settlement at the point.

In the meantime, "squatters" were moving in – European families, mostly of French descent, came to avail themselves of the abundant fish at the point. Some also began small-scale farming, growing staples such as potatoes, beans, and corn. More land was cleared over time and, taking advantage of the mild weather, grapes were planted! Animals – mainly pigs – were allowed to graze openly, which damaged the natural vegetation. The wide assortment

of wild animals, such as bear, deer, wild turkey, muskrat, and ruffled grouse attracted hunters and trappers.

It was a group of duck hunters / enthusiasts who saw the value of creating a preserve at the point. The founding members of The Great Lakes Ornithological Club were able to convince the federal government that action to protect the area was justified. Point Pelee National Park of Canada was created by a federal government order-in-council on May 29, 1918.

A. Answer these questions.

1. Why doesn't Point Pelee seem to be a part of Canada?

_____

_____

2. Why are trees in Point Pelee "dense with orange and black in the fall"?

_____

_____

3. What is so unique about the Point Pelee National Park, apart from the fact that it is located in the most southerly point on mainland Canada?

_____

_____

4. Why does the writer describe the early European families that settled in Point Pelee as "squatters"?

_____

_____

5. How did Point Pelee become a national park?

_____

_____

6. Why do you think there is "an unrivalled collection of plants and animals in a wide range of habitats" in Point Pelee that cannot be found anywhere else in Canada?

_____

_____

B. Read the clues and complete the crossword puzzle with words from the passage.

Across

A. battles

B. growing healthily

C. native

D. small area

E. the ability to see what will happen and take appropriate action

F. only one of its kind

G. a pleasant place surrounded by less desirable places

Down

1. survey to find out the population

2. carrying boats, goods, etc. overland from one navigable water to another

3. those occupying lands without legal rights

4. moving from one place to another

5. unequalled; cannot be matched

C. **Imagine you operate a Bed & Breakfast close to Point Pelee National Park. Write a short article in the local newsletter telling tourists what they can do at the park.**

There are many things to see and do at Point Pelee National Park.

_____

_____

_____

_____

_____

_____

_____

_____

_____

_____

_____

_____

_____

_____

_____

_____

_____

_____

The Art of Cubism

Are you an artist? Are you interested in art in all, or some, of its forms? It is always interesting to examine the evolution of the various forms of art, as well as innovations. "Cubism" is one well-known innovation in the world of art. It started as a new way of painting pictures, and went on to influence other artists, such as sculptors, musicians – and even writers!

Cubism began as an idea between two painters in Paris at the beginning of the 20th century, Georges Braque and Pablo Picasso. For decades previously, the art of France was mainly characterized as Impressionist, with bright and vivid colours, emphasizing the quality of light upon the subject, which was often people in outdoor settings, and landscapes. Braque and Picasso wanted to start looking at objects and people in a different way through their art. It was as if they were deconstructing their subject, and re-assembling it in an abstract way, usually with an assortment of shapes and angles with very little sense of depth in the picture. The colours were, when compared to the brilliant hues of Impressionism, rather monochromatic and dull.

The term "Cubism" came about in 1908 when a French art critic described a painting by Braque as being "full of little cubes". Soon other artists began experimenting with this interesting style, and a new movement, or "school", in painting was underway. Other artists took Cubism in different directions, and Braque and Picasso themselves developed several distinct phases. Around 1912, Picasso started experimenting with the inclusion of other objects in his paintings, such as chair caning, wood, and newspaper, using glue and paint. Of course, we see this today as the beginnings of the craft form called "collage", but at the time it was viewed as a significant moment in the evolution of two-dimensional art. They would also mix their media: adding shadows using charcoal, using combs to rake through the paint, and sprinkling on sand for added texture.

Cubism in music soon followed, with the development of an avant-garde style of music that sounded somewhat disjointed and irregular. In 1919, the famed composer Igor Stravinsky (who was living in Paris at the time) wrote a Cubist composition called Piano-Rag-Music, which incorporated popular jazzy Ragtime sounds with darker music inspired by his Russian homeland. Chamber music is obviously influenced by the Cubist movement.

A Cubist style of literature developed among writers living in Paris. Not only did they experiment with grammar and punctuation, but they also created written works using postcards, calligraphy, musical notation, and collage. One could easily say that today's graphic novels, so popular among young readers, are a form of Cubist literature. Do you agree?

A. In point form, compare Braque and Picasso's works with those of the Impressionists.

Braque and Picasso's Works	Impressionists' Works
_____	_____
_____	_____
_____	_____
_____	_____
_____	_____
_____	_____

B. Answer these questions.

1. How did the term "Cubism" come about?

   _____

   _____

2. How did Picasso start with the craft form which we call "collage" today?

   _____

   _____

3. What are the characteristics of Cubist music?

   _____

   _____

Your View

Do you agree with the writer that today's graphic novels are a kind of Cubist literature? Why or why not?

_____

_____

_____

_____

_____

C. Write the root word of each of the following.

1. evolution _____   2. cubism _____

3. characterized _____   4. Impressionist _____

5. deconstructing _____   6. different _____

D. Write sentences of your own to show that you understand the meanings of the following words.

1. vivid _____

_____

2. abstract _____

_____

3. monochromatic _____

_____

4. hues _____

_____

E. **Write a paragraph about the young Picasso based on the following points. Use descriptive words to enrich your writing.**

- *Picasso's father was called Jose Ruíz.*

- *Jose Ruíz was a painter.*

- *Jose Ruíz specialized in the naturalistic depiction of birds.*

- *Jose Ruíz was also a professor of art at the School of Crafts and a curator of a local museum.*

- *The young Picasso liked drawing from an early age.*

- *Picasso had his first formal academic art training from his father.*

- *Picasso attended carpenter schools throughout his childhood.*

- *Picasso never finished his college-level course of study at the Academy of Arts (Academia de San Fernando) in Madrid.*

- *Picasso left the Academy after less than a year.*

Section 2

Grammar

1 Subject-Verb Agreement

Simply put, **subject-verb agreement** means that a singular subject takes a singular verb and a plural subject demands a plural verb.

Examples: He <u>don't know</u> what he's doing. (✗)
He doesn't know what he's doing. (✔)

There <u>has been</u> a lot of rumours about Mr. Blake's departure. (✗)
There have been a lot of rumours about Mr. Blake's departure. (✔)

 Verbs for Indefinite Pronouns

Although **indefinite pronouns** such as "everyone" and "everybody" appear to be plural, they are singular and therefore take a singular verb. Sometimes, there may be phrases that contain plural words between the indefinite pronoun and its verb, but still we need to use a singular verb.

A. Read to see if the subject-verb agreement in the following sentences is right. If not, rewrite the sentences in the space provided.

1. Everyone involved in the play were happy to learn that all the tickets were sold out.

   _____

2. I don't think there is anyone here who can resolve the matter as well as you.

   _____

3. Some of the judges does not like the criteria given to them.

   _____

4. Each of the team members are reminded to attend the practice session.

   _____

5. Everybody know that it is wrong to take advantage of someone who actually need your help.

   _____

6. Since there wasn't anyone they could trust, they did it on their own.

   _____

7. Someone among the children have left the book here.

   _____

"Either" and "Neither"

Used as a subject alone, both "**either**" and "**neither**" stay singular and take a singular verb. However, when "either" and "neither" are used as correlative conjunctions, the subject that is closer to the verb determines whether the verb is singular or plural.

B. Complete the following sentences with the correct form of the verbs in parentheses.

1. Neither of the twin sisters _____ (like) the dress.

2. Either you or your stand-in _____ (have) to take up the task.

3. _____ (have) either the principal or the teachers been informed of the incident?

4. Either of them _____ (need) to decide if the project should proceed.

5. Neither the driver nor the passengers _____ (be) willing to come forward.

Fractional Expressions

In sentences with **fractional expressions**, what is being measured will determine whether to use a singular verb (for uncountable nouns) or a plural verb (for countable nouns).

C. Complete the following sentences with the correct form of the verbs in parentheses.

1. A third of the stock _____ (be) stolen last night.

2. Of all the applicants selected for interview, more than 60% _____ (live) within 15 kilometres from our office.

3. A majority of those in attendance _____ (say) that they will return for the debriefing next week.

4. Four-fifths of the water consumption _____ (be) for washing.

5. Only a minority of the voters _____ (not want) to see him elected.

"As well as" and "Together with"

While phrases such as "**as well as**" and "**together with**" seem to be used for joining subjects, they are not conjunctions. They should therefore be treated as separate phrases when we consider whether to use singular or plural verbs.

D. Choose the correct verb to complete each of the following sentences.

1. I, along with Mike and Timothy, _____ (am/are) considering a trip to the Rockies this summer.

2. Some of the food, as well as the paper cups and plates, _____ (was/were) left lying around.

3. The mayor, together with his staff, _____ (want/wants) to set up a special fund for renovating the building.

4. All the team members, including the coach, _____ (is/are) invited to the city hall.

5. Keith, as well as Greg Greene of the Eagles, _____ (stands/stand) a good chance to be the Player of the Week.

E. Read the following text and underline the mistakes in subject-verb agreement. Write the correct verb above the mistake.

Jim Carrey is one of those who never gives up their hopes and ambitions. In fact, when he was just ten years old, Carrey mailed his résumé to The Carol Burnett Show in the hope of joining them as a comedian! Noticing his talent, Carrey's high school teachers gave him a few minutes at the end of each school day to do a stand-up comedy for his classmates. It was certainly a great way to wrap up the day as everyone were entertained.

When Carrey was 13 years old, his father lost his job. He, as well as his father, were forced to move out of their house and live in their van instead. To help out, Carrey began working eight-hour shifts each day after school. The long hours exhausted Carrey and left him with little time to focus on homework and studies. This took a toll on Carrey's grades. To motivate himself, he once wrote a cheque for $20 million and vowed that he would cash it in some day. Both Jim himself and his father was confident that Carrey could make it. Sadly though, his father passed away a few years later. Carrey then put the cheque inside the pocket of his father's funeral clothes. Years later, Jim finally made it big in Hollywood as a comedian. Most of the Canadians, be they Jim's fans or not, admires his fighting spirit and his strong desire to succeed.

F. Make sentences with the following words and phrases to show your understanding of subject-verb agreement.

1. each of _____

2. two-thirds _____

3. as well as _____

4. everybody _____

5. either...or _____

6. neither of _____

7. of all the _____

2 Quantifiers and Determiners

 **Quantifiers**
· · · · · · · · · · · · · ·

Quantifiers are words that indicate quantity, i.e. how many or how much. They precede and modify nouns.

Examples: *There were just <u>a few</u> passengers on the night train.*

There is <u>not much</u> work left to do.

A. **Put the following quantifiers in the appropriate categories.**

| many | not much | a few | some | several |

| a lot of | a couple of | a bit of | a great deal of | a lack of |

| none of | enough | a little | all of | plenty of |

For Countable Nouns	For Uncountable Nouns	For both Countable Nouns and Uncountable Nouns

B. **Complete the following sentences with suitable quantifiers.**

1. I don't think there will be too _____ visitors to the fair since the weather is not good for the next _____ days. There will be _____ rain.

2. Since there was only _____
    food left in the fridge, we decided to go
    grocery shopping.   Mom bought
    _____ vegetables and meat,
    enough for the whole week. I bought
    _____ apples – one for a day.
    As the saying goes: "An apple a day keeps
    the doctor away."

3. They had _____ a problem installing the device.
    _____ the team members had done it before, and in the
    absence of _____ information, they could not figure out the
    best way to do it.

"Little" and "a Little" / "Few" and "a Few"

"**Little**" and "**a little**" are for use with uncountable nouns whereas "**few**" and "**a few**" are for use with countable nouns. While they all show quantity, both "little" and "few" have the implication of "not having enough".

C. **For the following sentences, decide whether to use "little", "a little", "few", or "a few".**

1. Josh has _____ friends at school; he doesn't socialize much.

2. The results will be announced in _____ days.

3. They had _____ left after the shopping spree.

4. _____ people realized the severity of the problem. They didn't see the need of prompt action.

5. He was _____ shocked to learn that he had not been chosen.

6. Here are _____ tips that you may find useful.

2 Quantifiers and Determiners

Determiners

Determiners are words that modify nouns, like what adjectives do. The following are categorized as determiners:

- Articles (a, an, the)
- Possessive nouns (John's, his teacher's...)
- Possessive pronouns (his, her, your, their...)
- Indefinite pronouns (few, each, every, some...)
- Demonstrative pronouns (this, that, these, those, such...)
- Numbers (one, two, three...)

D. Complete the following sentences with the appropriate determiners.

1. _____ group of buildings over there is said to have been built more than _____ decade ago by _____ architect from Quebec. However, I don't remember _____ name.

2. _____ plan was drawn up by me, with the help of Mr. Blair. _____ nephew, Harold, also pitched in and helped us collect _____ relevant data. Mr. Blair then did _____ analysis. We are going to present _____ plan to _____ committee _____ Friday so that we can start _____ rolling early next week.

3. They finally came up with _____ alternative – to let Jeff take up _____ assignment. Although Jeff was not _____ best choice because he was relatively green, _____ present agreed that he should be able to do it right.

E. In the following text, correct the mistakes in the use of quantifiers and determiners and add in the missing quantifiers or determiners.

Basketball has developed into one of the most popular sports in the world, but did you know that almost three thousand years ago, people were already playing the game similar to basketball?

It all happened in Mexico, in area called the Yucatan Peninsula in the 7th century BCE. The game, called "pok-a-tok", was played in a court made with stone walls. There was a goal at every end made from a flat stone with hole in the middle. Like NBA games, "pok-a-tok" attracted much spectators.

In the game, the players had to get a rubber ball stuffed with "sacred" plants into the goal. There were many unusual rules. Unlike basketball players today, the "pok-a-tok" players could not handle the ball with hands. They were allowed to move the ball using only his hips, thighs, and knees! Try doing that with the ball and you'll know how skilful that players must have been. However skilful they might have been, though, they could never do the acrobatic slam dunk!

3 Modifiers

Modifiers

A **modifier** adds information to another element in the sentence. It can be an adjective or an adverb, or it can be a phrase or a clause functioning as an adjective or adverb. Adjectives modify nouns and pronouns whereas adverbs modify verbs, adjectives, other adverbs, and sometimes even clauses or whole sentences.

A. Read each of the following sentences and decide if there is any wrong use of modifiers. If there is, rewrite the sentence in the correct way.

1. The attack was simply a cowardly act.

    _____

2. The players tried real hard to turn the game around.

    _____

3. Steve isn't feeling too good; he has a mild fever.

    _____

4. In order not to be discovered, he walked into the room slow and quiet.

    _____

5. They are working hardly to make sure that they can meet the deadline.

    _____

6. He did it so bad that he dared not submit it to the committee.

    _____

7. She felt awkward to approach him for help.

    _____

8. The plan should have been more careful executed.

    _____

9. The refugees are in desperately need of food, clothing, and medicine.

    _____

"Good", "Well", "Bad", and "Badly"

"**Good**" and "**bad**" are adjectives whereas "**well**" and "**badly**" are adverbs. Note that "well" is an adjective when it refers to health condition.

B. Check the correct sentence in each group.

1. A   Nelly plays the violin well and she feels good about it.

   B   Nelly plays the violin good and she isn't that well with the piano.

   C   Nelly doesn't play the violin well but she is pretty well with the cello.

   D   Nelly is good at the piano; she plays it real good.

2. A   Mr. Wilkinson doesn't seem to feel good today; he looks pale.

   B   Mr. Wilkinson needs medication real bad.

   C   Mr. Wilkinson's health has gone from bad to worse.

   D   Mr. Wilkinson should be good again after the intensive treatment.

3. A   He felt badly for the blunder he had made.

   B   He did not feel well about the gaffe.

   C   He felt bad for causing us so much trouble.

   D   He admitted that it was a badly mistake that he had made.

C. Complete the following sentences with "good", "well", "bad", or "badly".

1. Katie thought that it was a _____ opportunity for her. If she did _____ , she would stand a chance to be one of the finalists. Last time, she did it so _____ that she was eliminated in the first round.

2. We consider it a _____ idea because we won't be able to get any support. We should think _____ and come up with a strategy that is _____ enough to win at least four votes. We shouldn't do too _____ then.

3 Modifiers

Dangling Modifiers

We refer to a modifier as "**dangling**" when it modifies something that it shouldn't be modifying.

Example: *Walking down the street, the morning air refreshed me.* (✗)
(The morning air can't walk down the street!)
Walking down the street, I found the morning air refreshing. (✔)

When we begin a sentence with a modifying word, phrase, or clause, we have to make sure what comes next can actually be modified by that modifier.

D. Read each pair of sentences and check the correct one.

1. A Fuming and puffing, the bulls chased the crowds down the streets and alleys.

    B Fuming and puffing, the crowds were chased by the bulls down the streets and alleys.

2. A The children were delighted by the dolphins dashing through the hoop.

    B Dashing through the hoop, the children were delighted by the dolphins.

3. A He likes to have light music in the background doing his work.

    B He likes to have light music in the background while doing his work.

4. A Spending too much on luxuries, Cindy soon found that her salary just wasn't enough.

    B Spending too much on luxuries, Cindy's salary just wasn't enough.

5. A Without anything better to do, we decided to play video games at Kelly's home.

    B Without anything better to do, playing video games at Kelly's home seemed good.

6. A To be able to complete the marathon, the participant must know how to conserve energy and when to accelerate.

    B To be able to complete the marathon, knowing how to conserve energy and when to accelerate is important.

7.　A　To apply for the job, a résumé, together with a covering letter, should be submitted to the personnel manager on or before Friday.

　　　B　To apply for the job, an applicant must submit a résumé, together with a covering letter, to the personnel manager on or before Friday.

E.　Rewrite the following sentences so that they do not have dangling modifiers.

1.　To train a dog to be obedient, patience is useful.

_____

_____

2.　When taking a grammar quiz, concentration is everything.

_____

_____

3.　To be ready for the game, more practice is needed.

_____

4.　After washing my car, it sparkled like new.

_____

5.　After talking with the veterinarian, our dog needed surgery.

_____

6.　Having worked for the company for more than three decades, the manager fired Mr. Sutherland.

_____

7.　Before leaving for work, my cat played with me for a while.

_____

8.　To conserve energy, the air-conditioning system will be turned off after six.

_____

4 Prefixes and Suffixes

Word Roots

Many words in the English language are derived from Greek and Latin roots. Knowing these roots helps us grasp the meaning of words. It also enables us to see how words are often arranged in families with similar characteristics.

Example: *The Latin root "bio" means "life" – English words such as "biology" and "biography" are derived from it.*

A. Based on the meaning of each of the following word roots, give at least two English words that are derived from it.

Word Root	Meaning	Derivative
1. geo	earth	
2. audi	to hear	
3. manu	hand	
4. meter	measure	
5. tele	far off	
6. path	feeling	
7. astro	star	
8. bene	well	
9. op	work	
10. jur	law	
11. phys	body, nature	
12. fer	to carry	

Prefixes

The word "**prefix**" is made up of the base word "fix" (which means "attach") and the prefix "pre" (which means "before"). Prefix, therefore, means "to attach before".

B. Deduce the meaning of the prefixes by referring to the words given.

1. **semi**final **hemi**sphere

   Meaning: _____

2. **dis**arm **de**activate

   Meaning: _____

3. **uni**lateral **mono**chrome

   Meaning: _____

4. **re**write **re**submit

   Meaning: _____

5. **bi**cycle **di**lemma

   Meaning: _____

6. **super**impose **super**vise

   Meaning: _____

7. **kilo**metre **milli**gram

   Meaning: _____

8. **circum**ference **circum**vent

   Meaning: _____

9. **cent**ury **centi**metre

   Meaning: _____

10. **multi**ple **multi**function

    Meaning: _____

11. **un**favourable **im**possible

    Meaning: _____

12. **trans**port **trans**fer

    Meaning: _____

13. **tri**angle **tri**logy

    Meaning: _____

14. **inter**national **inter**ject

    Meaning: _____

15. **mis**fit **mis**behave

    Meaning: _____

16. **col**laborate **co**hesive

    Meaning: _____

17. **anti**clockwise **counter**propose

    Meaning: _____

18. **pre**view **pre**vent

    Meaning: _____

4   Prefixes and Suffixes

Suffixes

A **suffix** modifies the meaning of a word and often determines its function in a sentence.

Example: *sing (verb)*

sing<u>er</u> (noun)

sing<u>ing</u> (participle)

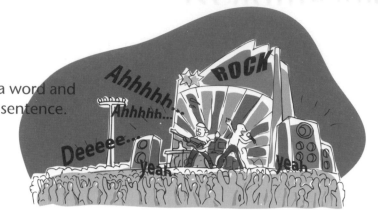

C. **Create as many derivatives as you can by adding suffixes to each of the following words.**

1. care

    _____

2. like

    _____

3. sharp

    _____

4. depend

    _____

5. watch

    _____

6. fear

    _____

7. nation

    _____

8. pretend

    _____

9. friend

    _____

D. Add a prefix and then a suffix to each of the following words. Write a sentence with each of the two newly-formed words.

1. caution

   a. _____

   b. _____

2. social

   a. _____

   b. _____

3. generate

   a. _____

   b. _____

4. behave

   a. _____

   b. _____

5. legal

   a. _____

   b. _____

6. possible

   a. _____

   b. _____

7. regulate

   a. _____

   b. _____

5 Tricky Words

Easily Confused Words

Sometimes we may take one word for another because the words sound almost the same, look similar, or they are related in meanings.

A. Complete the following sentences with the appropriate words provided.

1. imminent / eminent

    a. They didn't suspect any _____ danger.

    b. The audience was impressed by the

        _____ scientist.

2. lose / loose

    a. Don't _____ hope; there's one more inning to go.

    b. The dentist examined his _____ tooth.

3. adopt / adapt

    a. The team has agreed to _____ the new training schedule.

    b. The scriptwriter is planning to _____ his novel for the screen.

4. respectable / respectful

    a. The new student is from a _____ family.

    b. She is always _____ to her parents.

5. effect / affect

    a. The soothing music should have a positive _____ on their behaviour.

    b. I don't think the music can _____ their behaviour so much.

B. In each of the following sentences, replace the underlined word with a more appropriate word.

1. The principal believed that neither Tim <u>or</u> Eva should be held responsible.

   _____

2. He was <u>famous</u> for his anti-social behaviour.

   _____

3. They were so <u>anxious</u> when the star player came and signed on their caps.

   _____

4. <u>Beside</u> Timmy, I think that Rob, Cecil, and Sam were all involved.

   _____

5. The man threatened him with a knife and <u>stole</u> his wallet.

   _____

6. She should be <u>sensitive</u> enough not to repeat the same mistake.

   _____

7. His <u>childish</u> curiosity enables him to stay creative and adventurous.

   _____

C. Write sentences to show the difference in meaning between each pair of words. When in doubt, look them up in the dictionary.

1. lie / lay

   _____

   _____

2. rise / raise

   _____

   _____

3. service / serve

   _____

   _____

D. **The following are some cases of tricky usage. Read the explanations and complete the sentences with the correct choices.**

1. **in** and **into**

   "In" is to indicate the location whereas "into" shows the movement: from outside to inside.

   a. Mustering his courage, he finally made the jump and dived _____ the pool.

   b. Hank told me that he had placed all the documents _____ the cabinet.

2. **it's** and **its**

   "It's" is the contracted form for "it is" whereas "its" is a possessive adjective.

   a. The kitten kept chasing _____ tail.

   b. While _____ certainly worth going for, you should think about the way to do it.

3. **fewer** and **less**

   "Fewer" refers to units of things whereas "less" refers to amount.

   a. There were _____ spectators than I had expected.

   b. My father usually goes to work before six when the traffic is _____ congested.

4. **each other** and **one another**

   "Each other" refers to two people whereas "one another" refers to more than two people.

   a. Although they are twin sisters, they always point an accusing finger at _____ .

   b. The players blamed _____ for the humiliating loss.

5. **wander** and **wonder**

"Wander" means walking around without a purpose whereas "wonder" means worried or suspicious about something.

a. They are supposed to _____ around here.

b. I _____ whether or not we can complete it on time.

6. **than** and **then**

"Than" is used for comparison whereas "then" means afterwards.

a. I opened the safe; _____ I noticed that something was missing – it was the gold bracelet.

b. To his fans, the hall-of-fame player was larger _____ life.

E. **Read the following text and underline the wrongly-used words. Write the appropriate words above them.**

If you look at a medieval map of the world, you might wander why there are less continents then a modern map and why there is a large section labelled as "the unknown".

The truth is, in the old days people usually sought advise from those respectful priests, who, in turn, would refer to the Bible for answers. Since the Bible often mentioned the four corners of the Earth, it was assumed than that the world was square and flat.

People were actually afraid to sail too far out in the ocean for fear that they might sail right off the edge of the world! It was quite some time before people excepted that the world was not flat.

6 Some Less Common Tenses

Future Perfect

The **future perfect** is made up of "will have" + past participle or "is/am/are" + "going to have" + past participle. It is used to denote that something will occur before another action in the future. It can also be used to show that something will happen before a specific time in the future.

Examples: *By the time I finish my second piano lesson, I <u>will have learned</u> how to play this tune.*

I <u>am going to have learned</u> how to play this tune after my second piano lesson.

A. Check the sentences in which the future perfect is used properly.

1. Before he arrives, they will have got everything ready. _____

2. Lilian will have arrived in Italy by ten unless her flight is delayed. _____

3. If he has asked me personally, I will have agreed to help. _____

4. When he will have bought the tickets, we can go to the show together. _____

5. By June next year, his brother will have completed his undergraduate studies. _____

6. If the pitcher will have made fewer mistakes, our team will win the game. _____

7. We will have been happy for you when you are going to have told us the news. _____

8. They will have painted the house if you allow them to work all day there. _____

9. It's already too late. Mr. Silver will have left by the time we reach his office. _____

10. They are going to have mastered the skill when they complete the training. _____

Past Perfect

The **past perfect**, made up of "had" + past participle, is used to indicate that something happened before another event in the past. It can also be used to show something that happened before a specific time in the past.

Example: *We <u>had never met</u> each other before we <u>joined</u> the team in 1999.*
               (past perfect)   (past)

B. Check the sentences with the proper use of tenses.

1. Although he told me everything, I had not revealed it to anyone.   _____

2. Let's make sure that they had read over it before we send it out.   _____

3. After the technician had set up the system, Mr. Fernandez started testing it.   _____

4. We had almost finished the work when he volunteered to help.   _____

5. Before the police arrested him, they had interviewed many witnesses.   _____

C. Complete the following sentences with the correct form of the verbs provided.

1. By the time the family _____ (reach) the station, the train _____ (depart).

2. The committee _____ (meet) once to discuss the issue before yesterday's meeting.

3. Before they _____ (decide) to break the news to her, Mrs. Brightman _____ (remind) them to do it tactfully.

4. After they _____ (finish) the project, they _____ (go) out for a walk.

5. Although they _____ (come) in early, the night-shift workers _____ (already leave).

6 Some Less Common Tenses

"Used to" and "Would always"

Both "**used to**" and "**would always**" are used to show old habits. "Used to" expresses the idea that something was an old habit but it is not done anymore. It can also be used to talk about past facts that are no longer true. "Would always", on the other hand, suggests that someone willingly acted that way and it is often used to express annoyance or amusement at the habit.

"Am/is/are used to"

This is used to describe an existing habit of doing things. Note that we have to use a gerund after it.

D. Complete the following.

1. Write three things that you used to do. Say when you did these things and why you no longer do them.

    a. _____

    b. _____

    c. _____

2. Use "would always" to write about three things your friends did in the past that you find unusual.

    a. _____

    b. _____

    c. _____

3. Write three things that you or your friends are used to doing.

    a. _____

    b. _____

    c. _____

E. Read the following text and correct the misused verb tenses. Write the correct form above the mistakes.

The Boeing 747 is often referred to as the Jumbo Jet. With its upper-deck hump, the Jumbo Jet had been the most recognizable icon of air travel. It is the largest passenger plane, as it is used to be able to accommodate a maximum of 524 passengers. Soon, however, it will have become the second largest, when the Airbus A380 is officially put into service.

Unlike the hump on the Jumbo Jet, the A380's upper deck extends along the entire length of the fuselage. This allows for a spacious cabin with 50% more floor space than the Boeing 747. In fact, an A380 jet plane can be configured to carry more than 850 passengers! No wonder people are used to calling it the Superjumbo. Commercial flights had been scheduled to begin in 2007 after lengthy delays due to technical glitches.

Both the 747 and the A380 can fly at high-subsonic speeds of 900 kilometres per hour, but in terms of intercontinental range, the A380 can fly non-stop for 15 000 km while the 747's maximum range is 13 000 km.

So, after the A380, what will have been the next big thing that flies in the air?

7 Use of Capital Letters

What to Capitalize

- the first word of every sentence, except for one that is in parentheses within another sentence
- names of family relations when used as substitutes for names
- names of people and places, but not directions
- titles when used before names but not after names
- days of the week, months, holidays, and special events

A. Read the following sentences to see if there are any mistakes in capitalization. Rewrite the sentences where mistakes are found.

1. The Lunar new year is celebrated not only by the Chinese but also by the japanese.

   _____

   _____

2. Mark told his mom that he would have a game of soccer with his classmates after school.

   _____

3. No one seemed to have any idea of the origin of April fool's day.

   _____

4. When we finally reached the Hotel, we were told that all the rooms had been booked.

   _____

5. The 2010 winter olympics will be held in Vancouver, British columbia.

   _____

6. Mr. Jones was the Chairman of the Committee between 2003 and 2005.

   _____

7. The principal greeted Officer Powell, who came to talk to us on crime prevention.

   _____

B. Rewrite the following sentences and apply capitalization wherever needed.

1. last weekend, uncle bob took us to an ice-fishing trip up north.

    _____

2. in fall, the migratory birds fly south to mexico to stay away from the bitter cold in winter.

    _____

3. the principal showed the new teacher, mrs. williamson, the way to the library.

    _____

4. mom is excited about having a chance to meet up with aunt sue and uncle joe but dad doesn't seem to be too enthusiastic about it.

    _____

5. bahrain is a borderless island country in the persian gulf in the middle east.

    _____

6. this year's parents' night will be held on september 19 and jonathan is on the organizing committee.

    _____

7. they enjoy math lessons because they find their math teacher both knowledgeable and entertaining.

    _____

8. he is planning to move to a little town called lakeview, which is about an hour's drive from belville.

    _____

9. she introduced me to her father (he looked much younger than i'd thought) and we had a good chat.

    _____

10. mrs. patterson headed south down the road and then turned into wellington avenue.

    _____

7 Use of Capital Letters

Rules for Titles

In titles, we usually capitalize all the words except articles, prepositions, and coordinating conjunctions.

C. Rewrite the following titles in the proper form.

1. 101 ways to decorate your living room

    _____

2. what your doctor doesn't want you to know

    _____

3. the old man and the sea

    _____

4. the revenge of the robots

    _____

5. all you want to know about the web

    _____

6. dead or alive

    _____

7. the bottom of the ninth

    _____

8. the bermuda triangle – fact or fiction

    _____

9. somewhere out there

    _____

10. what dogs like and dislike

    _____

D. Read the following text and underline the mistakes in capitalization. Write the correct form above the mistake.

The Winter Olympics is finally returning to north America eight years after Salt lake city hosted the games in 2002. In 2010, Vancouver will be hosting the games, which will be the Third Olympics hosted by Canada (Previously, Canada was home to the 1976 summer Olympics in Montreal and the 1988 Winter Olympics in Calgary). And for the first time ever, the opening and closing Ceremonies for a Winter Olympics will be held indoors.

Before bidding for hosting the games, Vancouver's residents were asked in a Referendum whether they accepted the responsibilities of the Host City should it win its bid. Sixty-four Percent of the residents accepted the challenge. It was the first time such a Referendum had been successful. Vancouver finally won the bidding process to host the Olympics on July 2, 2003.

The Canadian Olympic Committee has pledged to win the most Gold Medals at the 2010 Winter Olympics. To achieve this lofty goal, *Own The Podium 2010* has been launched. It is a collaborative effort supported by all of Canada's winter national sport federations. The focus is to provide additional resources and high-performance programming for Canadian athletes and coaches to help Canadian athletes achieve podium success in 2010.

8 Some More Members of the Punctuation Family

The three most-used punctuation marks are: the comma, the period, and the question mark. But punctuation does not stop with these three; there are many more less-used but equally useful punctuation marks that can help keep our writing clear and orderly.

The Colon

We use a **colon** to set off a list, an explanation, or a quotation, much like a pointer telling the reader what is about to follow the main part of the sentence.

Example: *Your composition should include the following: the introduction, the body, and the conclusion.*

A. Add a colon in each of the following sentences.

1. Remember what John F. Kennedy said "We need men who can dream of things that never were."

2. The coach needed two things from us our desire to win and our faith in him.

3. Few realized that the plan had one major flaw it involved too much investment at the outset.

4. They knew what to do next report the case to the principal.

5. Do you know who said this "Truth is what stands the test of experience"?

6. If we analyze a paragraph, we often notice these three components the topic sentence, the supporting details, and the concluding sentence.

7. There remained one problem we had to win Jeffrey over.

8. The zoo expects some more animals to arrive in the next couple of days two cheetahs, one gorilla, one kangaroo, and six penguins.

We can also use a dash in place of a colon to set off lists and explanations in informal writing.

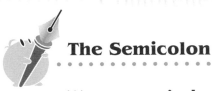

The Semicolon

We use a **semicolon** to:

- sort out a long list

  Example: *There were representatives from Toronto, Ontario; Charlottetown, Prince Edward Island; Victoria, British Columbia, and Calgary, Alberta.*

- separate closely related independent clauses

  Example: *The train is scheduled to arrive at 7:35 a.m. every day; it is always on schedule.*

B. Add commas, semicolons, or colons in appropriate places.

1. The batter keyed up he waited patiently for the pitch.

2. The couple invited several distinguished guests to the reception Mrs. Weir Principal of St. Peter's School Professor Swire the University of Toronto Mr. Sam Watson MPP Scarborough East and David Nunn Executive Director The Knowledge Bank Ontario Chapter.

3. There was only one thing remaining on her to-do list make an appointment with Mr. Cook on or before Tuesday.

4. He didn't sleep well it was too hot and humid.

5. As soon as she realized the problem, she asked for her father's help it was too late though.

6. The doctor can tell that there is something wrong with her she is panting.

7. No one knew what was going on the situation simply ran out of control.

8. You need the following to succeed motivation commitment and perseverance.

9. Grandmother used to get up very early she enjoyed the atmosphere of daybreak.

10. We stuffed our backpacks with everything snacks utensils tools and even shoes!

8   Some More Members of the Punctuation Family

Parentheses

We use **parentheses** to include additional information within a sentence that wouldn't normally fit into the flow of our text.

Example: *The committee (a total of 12 members) agreed that a three-member panel be set up immediately to deal with the issue.*

Note that parentheses tend to de-emphasize text, making it less important.

C.   Read the following text.   Add parentheses where appropriate.

Albert Einstein March 14, 1879 – April 18, 1955 is considered one of the greatest physicists of all time. He is best known as the creator of the theory of relativity specifically E=mc². In fact, the name "Einstein" has become synonymous with great intelligence and genius.

At his birth, Albert's mother was worried about her infant: his head was so large and oddly shaped! Einstein also spoke much later than the average child. He recalled that he did not begin speaking until the age of three and only did so hesitantly even beyond the age of nine. Because of Einstein's late speech development and his later childhood tendency to ignore any subject in school that bored him focusing instead only on what interested him, some observers at the time suggested that he might be retarded.

When Einstein was young probably at the age of five, his father showed him a small pocket compass, and Einstein believed that the needle must have been affected by something in empty space. He later described the experience as one of the most revelatory events of his life.

Quotation Marks

We use **quotation marks** to set off material that represents quoted or spoken language. Quotation marks also set off the titles of short stories, poems, and articles.

Examples: The teacher said, "You may refer to the handout I gave out yesterday."

Is "The Guide to Scuba Diving" still with you?

D. Add quotation marks in each of the following questions and statements.

1. I don't know what you mean by categorically.

2. L.M. Montgomery's Anne of Green Gables was first published in 1908.

3. Perhaps you should clarify with Mrs. Sutherland the term stimulated emission.

4. The reporter asked Where were you when the accident happened'?

5. What is the expected increase rate? asked the manager.

6. They said Dr. Seuss used only 50 words to write Green Eggs and Ham.

7. In this context, pristine means remaining in a pure state.

8. How can you say that you have nothing to do with it? complained Fred.

9. When told not to make any more such mistakes, Jason rebuked Freedom is not worth having if it does not include the freedom to make mistakes.

10. She wrote a feature article entitled The Poverty Problem – a Time Bomb.

11. There is no way I can tell that this is a better alternative explained Barry.

12. Pride and Prejudice was written by Jane Austen, who also wrote Sense and Sensibility.

A. Choose the correct verb to complete each of the following sentences.

1. Everybody in class _____ (is/are) happy that Mrs. Kay is coming back to be the school librarian.

2. "_____ (Is/Are) there anyone here who knows how to use a scientific calculator?" asks Ryan.

3. Neither Tom nor his sisters _____ (know/knows) what the family dog is up to.

4. "_____ (Have/Has) either one of you thought about keeping *Snow Falling on Cedars* in the school library?" asks the principal.

5. More than three-quarters of the students _____ (think/thinks) the school needs a swimming pool.

6. A majority of the parents _____ (prefer/prefers) to have the council meeting on Thursday evenings.

7. My parents, together with Grandpa, _____ (want/wants) to give our basement a makeover.

8. My favourite movie this year, along with my brother's favourite, _____ (have/has) a very good shot at the Oscars.

9. Sara, as well as Julie, _____ (play/plays) jazz very well on the piano.

10. Everybody in the school, including the principal, _____ (is/are) hoping that the strike would be over soon.

B. Use the following to make sentences. Make sure there is subject-verb agreement.

1. neither of

_____

2. of all the

_____

3. together with

_____

4. 50%

_____

C. Read each pair of sentences and check the correct one.

1. A   There is plenty of lemonade for everyone on this very hot day!

    B   There are plenty of lemonade for everyone on this very hot day!

2. A   Jim will give me a few of his cookies if I give him a few of my pudding.

    B   Jim will give me a few of his cookies if I give him a bit of my pudding.

3. A   There are not enough vegetable sticks for the year-end party.

    B   There is only a little vegetable sticks for the year-end party.

4. A   To Samantha, it is never too much trouble to make a healthful snack.

    B   To Samantha, it is never too many troubles to make a heathful snack.

D. Complete the following sentences with the given modifiers.

hard	real	good	bad	quick
hardly	really	well	badly	quickly

1. Sara can _____ wait for the dance show to start.

2. Amanda _____ hopes that she will win the Citizenship Award.

3. In order to perform well, Billy thought long and _____ about his character in the school play.

4. It is too _____ that my best friend will miss Graduation Night.

5. "If you keep playing this game _____," says Jill's coach, "I'll have to pull you out."

6. "I'm a physiotherapist – for _____ !" My mom tries to convince our new acquaintance after having told too many jokes.

7. "Don't worry," says Grandma. "I'm in _____ health. I'm doing very

    _____ ."

8. Neal is _____ becoming a star on the basketball court. He is short but he makes _____ passes and very good shots.

E. Read each sentence and decide if there is any dangling modifier. If so, rewrite the sentence in the correct way.

1. When it comes to saving lives, every minute counts.

    _____

2. "To ski your personal best," advises Coach Simon, "visualize your ski run before you start."

    _____

    _____

3. Whistling down the garden path, a brilliant idea suddenly came to Bill.

    _____

4. Delighted by all the Christmas cheer, Grandma is wearing a rare smile.

    _____

5. With plenty of time to spare, another new cabinet is built by Jeff!

    _____

6. Having always been active, professional cyclist Marianne suffered no broken bones after her fall.

    _____

    _____

7. "When mixing the dough, make sure you don't overdo it," Mom says.

    _____

8. Cartwheeling across the field, the excitement can hardly be contained by Catherine!

    _____

    _____

9. To make this salad tasty, you need to add a dash of balsamic vinegar.

    _____

10. Daydreaming again, Mrs. Cook asked Rose why she was staring at the sky.

    _____

    _____

F.   Fill in the blanks with the correct determiners.

Every now and then, do you get 1._____ feeling that you have already

the / that

experienced in 2._____ dream what you are experiencing at

the / a

3._____ present moment – in other words, do you have "déjà vu" from

the / that

time to time? A friend of mine says 4._____ life is full of déjà vu. In

her / hers

elementary school, she told me 5._____ story: while living in another

such / this

country years ago, she had 6._____ dream in which she found herself

the / a

living in 7._____ house with 8._____ brown roof and yellow sidings.

a / the   that / a

When she moved here with her family, 9._____ home turned out to be

the / their

precisely 10._____ same house! One day in high school, she told me

a / that

another story: she dreamt that she was sharing a huge room with 11._____

one / two

other girls, and joked that maybe 12._____ would actually turn out to be

such / this

true someday. What do you know? When she lived on 13._____ own for

their / her

14._____ first time during university, she ended up sharing 15._____

a / the   a / that

same room with 16._____ same two girls! My friend thinks that déjà vu

the / that

happens to everybody, but that 17._____ people have poor memory of

the / some

18._____ dreams, while others remember them in great detail, like herself.

the / their

115

F.   Fill in the blanks with the correct determiners.

1.

2.

3.

4.

5.

6.

7.

8.

9.

10.

11.

12.

13.

14.

15.

16.

17.

18.

G. Check the sentence if the underlined word is used properly.

1. The "Biography" section is <u>besides</u> the "Travel" section. _____

2. "<u>Raise</u> your hand before you speak," says Mrs. Fells. _____

3. I <u>wonder</u> if you have some time to read this over for me? _____

4. This song is much longer <u>then</u> that one and is putting me to sleep! _____

5. In some countries, journalism is not a very <u>respectable</u> profession. _____

6. When there are <u>less</u> cars on the road, we will have cleaner air. _____

H. Group the following words by their root or prefix. Then choose two from each group to write sentences.

superscript   trilingual   telepathy   superintendent
triplets   superhero   trillium   television
tricycle   telephone   telegram   supernatural

1.

Prefix/Root Meaning	Word
three	
above	
far off	

2. a. _____

_____

b. _____

_____

c. _____

_____

I. **Complete each sentence with the correct tense of the given verb.**

1. By the time we finish our journey, Tom _____ (finish) his lunch!

2. Sheila _____ (master) oil painting by the end of her semester.

3. When Mom _____ (finish) making dinner, I will have eaten all the nuts on the table.

4. Alfred _____ (be) to Cairo before he met Barclay.

5. Before you even arrived, I _____ (hear) a lot about you.

6. Toby's dream _____ (come) true by the end of next summer!

7. Eunice _____ (volunteer) to help with the bake sale before anyone asked her.

8. The frog _____ (leap) back into the pond by the time you turned to look.

J. **Read the following text. Add semicolons, colons, parentheses, or quotation marks where appropriate.**

The collection of German and French fairy tales known as *Grimm's Fairy Tales* called *Children's and Household Tales* in English was published throughout the 1800s by Jacob and Wilhelm Grimm, two German brothers with an interest in ancient fairy tales. Many stories from their collection have enjoyed widespread appeal, such as Hansel and Gretel Sleeping Beauty Rapunzel Rumpelstiltskin The Golden Goose, and The Singing Bone. Because the brothers' father died when they were young, leaving the mother to take care of the family in harsh circumstances, some psychologists have argued that this influenced the way the Brothers Grimm presented the mother figure in their stories, like the stepmother in Sleeping Beauty and the wicked witch in Hansel and Gretel. Although the collection has been criticized for not being suitable for children as in the violence involved in punishing some of the villains, *Grimm's Fairy Tales* has a huge influence in literary culture it ranks behind only the Bible and the works of Shakespeare in sales, and has been translated into many different languages around the world.

9 Some Basic Spelling Rules

Basic Rule #1

Hey! Put "i" before "e", except after "c" and in words that rhyme with "hey".

Examples: die, receive, reign

A. Write five words or more in the appropriate boxes.

"i" before "e"	"e" before "i"	word rhyming with "hey"

Exceptions to Rule #1:

Basic Rule #2

Why? "Y" becomes "i" before adding an ending, except when the "y" follows a vowel or when the ending is "-ing".

Examples: varies, swayed, crying

B. Write five words or more in the appropriate boxes.

"y" becomes "i"	"y" follows a vowel	"-ing"

Basic Rule #3

Silent! Drop the silent "e" before adding an ending that begins with a vowel.

Example: intrigue – intriguing

Basic Rule #4

Double the ending consonant before adding an ending that begins with a vowel.

Example: remit – remittance

Basic Rule #5

Rule #4 does not apply when the word is accented on the first syllable.

Example: <u>fidget</u> – fidgeting

C. **Write five words or more that follow each of the rules above.**

Rule #3	Rule #4	Rule #5

D. **Cross out the misspelled words and write the correct spelling above them.**

decietful	feint	likelihood	worryed
hygiene	enterprising	plyed	inclinning
throbbing	plagueing	circulating	impending

E. Read the clues and complete the following crossword puzzle on tricky spelling.

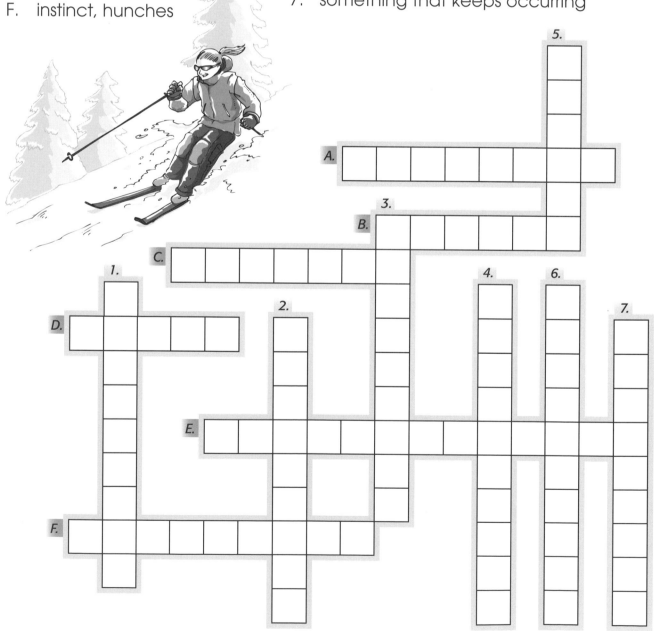

Across

A. forming a regular beat or pattern

B. adding colour to cloth

C. cheat

D. pale brown in colour

E. leaving what one should do until later

F. instinct, hunches

Down

1. having to rely on something

2. not being genuine

3. one that needs others' financial support

4. interesting, strange

5. a sport on snowy slopes

6. considering two or more things

7. something that keeps occurring

F. **Write sentences to show the difference in meaning between each pair of words that spell similarly. When in doubt, look them up in your dictionary.**

1. counsel / council

_____

_____

2. supercede / supersede

_____

_____

3. access / assess

_____

_____

4. simmer / shimmer

_____

_____

5. teeming / teaming

_____

_____

6. ascent / accent

_____

_____

7. hoot / hood

_____

_____

8. imminent / eminent

_____

_____

10 Phrases

Phrases

A **phrase** is a group of words that functions as one unit in a sentence. Each phrase has a word that links it to the rest of the sentence. That word is often referred to as the "head". Phrases can be classified by the type of head they take.

- A prepositional phrase has a preposition as head.
- A noun phrase has a noun as head.
- A verb phrase has a verb as head.
- An adjective phrase has an adjective as head.
- An adverbial phrase has an adverb as head.

A. Circle the head of each of the underlined phrases.

1. Which of these books are <u>of particular interest</u> to you?

2. They did not see <u>the little gemstone</u> behind the couch.

3. My sister plays the piano <u>after school</u>.

4. We <u>will be leaving</u> for Paris this Saturday.

5. For my birthday, she gave me <u>a heart-shaped box</u>.

6. Although she was nervous, she performed <u>surprisingly well</u>.

7. My cousin's neighbour fixed <u>the collapsed fence</u> for him.

8. His teacher thinks that he is a <u>very hard-working</u> student.

9. Sharon wiped clean the countertop <u>with a paper towel</u>.

10. Hardly anyone noticed what she <u>was wearing</u>.

11. <u>Under such circumstances</u>, I don't think it is wise to go on.

12. They were involved in <u>a serious car accident</u>.

B. **Identify each of the underlined phrases below. Write "PP" for prepositional phrase, "NP" for noun phrase, "VP" for verb phrase, "AP" for adjective phrase, and "AVP" for adverbial phrase.**

1. Look at <u>the little puppy</u> on the rug. Isn't it cute? ⎯⎯⎯⎯⎯

2. The book <u>on the shelf</u> belongs to Natasha. ⎯⎯⎯⎯⎯

3. The children were trying to climb <u>over the fence</u>. ⎯⎯⎯⎯⎯

4. Mrs. Saunders told them to approach it <u>very cautiously</u>. ⎯⎯⎯⎯⎯

5. The dog <u>jumped up and down</u> when he saw me. ⎯⎯⎯⎯⎯

6. There is <u>a shortage of food</u> after the severe flooding. ⎯⎯⎯⎯⎯

7. I must say your proposal is <u>very unusual and interesting</u>. ⎯⎯⎯⎯⎯

C. **Add words of your choice to the underlined words below to make adjective phrases, adverbial phrases, or noun phrases.**

1. The <u>man</u> somehow reminds me of Uncle John.

   ⎯⎯⎯⎯⎯⎯⎯⎯⎯⎯⎯⎯⎯⎯⎯⎯⎯⎯⎯⎯⎯⎯

2. The movie was <u>boring</u>; halfway through it, I was already dozing off!

   ⎯⎯⎯⎯⎯⎯⎯⎯⎯⎯⎯⎯⎯⎯⎯⎯⎯⎯⎯⎯⎯⎯

3. The way she did it was <u>unacceptable</u>.

   ⎯⎯⎯⎯⎯⎯⎯⎯⎯⎯⎯⎯⎯⎯⎯⎯⎯⎯⎯⎯⎯⎯

4. We took the <u>flight</u> to Quebec, which took us about two hours.

   ⎯⎯⎯⎯⎯⎯⎯⎯⎯⎯⎯⎯⎯⎯⎯⎯⎯⎯⎯⎯⎯⎯

5. Beth did <u>well</u> on the test.

   ⎯⎯⎯⎯⎯⎯⎯⎯⎯⎯⎯⎯⎯⎯⎯⎯⎯⎯⎯⎯⎯⎯

6. I hope you'll act <u>sensibly</u> next time.

   ⎯⎯⎯⎯⎯⎯⎯⎯⎯⎯⎯⎯⎯⎯⎯⎯⎯⎯⎯⎯⎯⎯

Adjective and Adjectival Phrases

An **adjective phrase** is a phrase that has an adjective as its head.

An **adjectival phrase**, however, can be any phrase that functions like an adjective.

Examples: It was <u>awfully silly</u> of you to tell such kind of joke.
(adjective phrase, with "silly" as its head)

It was a <u>two-hour</u> ride to the outskirts of the city.
(adjectival phrase, with words usually joined together by hyphens)

D. **Decide whether the underlined phrases in the following sentences are adjective phrases (ADJ) or adjectival (ADL) phrases.**

1. I'm sure you can do an <u>even better</u> job next time. _____

2. They will conduct an <u>in-depth</u> survey in early June. _____

3. All of us are receiving <u>on-the-job</u> training. _____

4. How can you expect a <u>six-year-old</u> boy to show you the way? _____

5. Wait until the shirt is <u>completely dry</u> before putting it on. _____

6. They made a <u>last-minute</u> decision to close the plant. _____

7. The children were <u>awfully sad</u> when they had to go. _____

E. **Complete the following sentences with adjectival phrases.**

1. We need _____ information on global warming.

2. Our flight experienced a _____ delay because of the snowstorm.

3. This is truly a _____ home theatre.

4. It is a _____ secret.

5. The _____ boots are too small for me.

6. The _____ snow really came as a surprise!

F. **Complete the following paragraph with phrases of your own. Identify the types of phrases used.**

This winter, our family went 1._____ to Québec City. We stayed at the Château Frontenac Hotel, which offers 2._____ of the Saint Lawrence River. Many of the city's attractions 3._____ east of the fortification walls. Visitors 4._____ can go through St. Louis Gate and St. Jean Gate from the modern section of Québec City. Old Québec City has a 5._____ feel that is unique in North America 6._____ and winding streets. There were 7._____ and restaurants. We bought 8._____ from a little shop there.

Types of Phrases

1. _____   2. _____

3. _____   4. _____

5. _____   6. _____

7. _____   8. _____

11 Adverbs, Adverb Phrases, and Adverb Clauses

Adverbs

An **adverb** modifies a verb, an adjective, or another adverb.

Examples: *The old man walked <u>slowly</u> down the street. (modifies the verb "walked")*

He walked in an <u>extremely</u> slow manner. (modifies the adjective "slow")

He walked <u>very</u> slowly. (modifies the adverb "slowly")

A. Add an adverb in each of the following sentences. Make any other necessary changes.

1. Although it was his first appearance in the show, he performed well.

    _____

2. She touched the little girl's head and spoke to her.

    _____

3. The teacher was satisfied with what our group had done.

    _____

4. He gave in and agreed to let us use the room on Saturday.

    _____

5. The chairman was happy that the plan had been executed.

    _____

6. As long as we tell her in advance, she will be able to join us.

    _____

7. I don't think we should go because it's already late.

    _____

8. Yesterday, they had a heated debate over whether or not to go ahead with the plan.

    _____

Adverb Phrases

An **adverb phrase** is a group of words (without a subject and a verb) functioning as an adverb. **Prepositional phrases** often have adverb functions (telling place and time, modifying the verb).

Examples: Greg and Shawn went <u>to the movies</u>. *(telling where they went)*

Mr. Mendoza is so busy that he often works <u>on weekends</u>. *(telling when Mr. Mendoza works)*

Infinitive phrases can act as adverbs too.

Example: She went straight into the room <u>to find out what was happening</u>. *(telling why she went into the room)*

B. Complete the following sentences with adverb phrases.

1. The firefighters dashed _____

2. They examined the specimen _____

3. Let's have a meeting _____

4. Samantha does not seem _____

5. They moved _____ last year.

6. My parents are happy _____

7. They have decided to have the party held _____

8. The guests will be here _____

9. The plane departed _____

10. They walked _____ to the third floor.

11. We were amazed _____

12. They dived into the water _____

13. Sasha rang the bell _____

14. We hoisted the flag _____

11 Adverbs, Adverb Phrases, and Adverb Clauses

Adverb Clauses

An **adverb clause** is a clause (containing a subject and a full verb) that functions as an adverb.

Examples: They had a game of basketball <u>yesterday</u>. (adverb)

They had a game of basketball <u>after school</u>. (adverb phrase)

They had a game of basketball <u>before they went home</u>. (adverb clause)

C. Put the underlined adverb clauses in the appropriate categories.

- He came early <u>so that he had some time to rehearse</u>.

- <u>Before the coach arrived</u>, they were just sitting there chatting.

- Mrs. Winter was angry <u>because Matt and Sue misbehaved in class</u>.

- <u>Wherever he goes</u>, he brings along his lucky charm – a gold coin given him by his grandfather.

- <u>If you listened to me</u>, you would not get yourself into trouble.

- <u>Although we seldom see each other now</u>, we remain best friends.

1. Adverb Clause of Place

    _____

2. Adverb Clause of Time

    _____

3. Adverb Clause of Reason

    _____

4. Adverb Clause of Purpose

    _____

5. Adverb Clause of Contrast

    _____

6. Adverb Clause of Condition

    _____

D. Underline the adverb clauses in the following text.

Have you been to an ice hotel before? In January each year, there is one built near Montmorency Falls, Quebec when the temperature is low enough. Come April and the hotel will melt.

The walls of the ice hotel are more than a metre thick so that it is structurally safe. Although the beds in the ice hotel are all made of ice blocks, you won't feel cold because they are lined with deer furs and covered with mattresses and arctic sleeping bags. All other furniture is made of ice, too. In addition to using ice glasses, the bar also serves cold cuts on ice plates. The bathrooms are heated, but they are in a separate insulated structure.

It is quite an experience spending a night in a hotel made of ice – to enjoy the beauty of winter. The ice hotel is absolutely spectacular, especially when it is all lit up at night. There is one thing that is somewhat annoying, though: if you feel the urge to go to the bathroom in the middle of the night, you'll have to get dressed to bear the cold along the corridor leading to the heated bathrooms.

12 Superfluous Words and Phrases

Clear and Concise Writing

Clear and **concise** writing requires using the right expressions and saying what we intend to, rather than loading our sentences with superfluous words and phrases.

Example: <u>The reason why</u> we went without him <u>was</u> because he was late for almost an hour.

We went without him because he was late for almost an hour.

A. Think of a word to replace each of the superfluous phrases below.

1. at this point in time
   _____

2. as to whether
   _____

3. due to the fact that
   _____

4. each and every
   _____

5. in the absence of
   _____

6. so as to
   _____

7. in conjunction with
   _____

8. on account of
   _____

9. a large proportion of
   _____

10. in the event that
    _____

11. by virtue of the fact that
    _____

12. with the exception of
    _____

B. Cross out the superfluous words or phrases to make the sentences more concise.

1. The great white shark cannot compare with the blue whale in terms of size.

2. In my opinion, I think we cannot find a better alternative than this.

130

3. He is the kind of man who always puts his foot in his mouth.

4. The barrel, as a matter of fact, was much larger than I had expected.

5. Hugh promised never to repeat the mistake again.

6. The troop was surrounded on all sides by the enemy.

7. The chairman assured us that he would consider our personal opinions.

8. The parcel was returned back to me because of the wrong address.

9. The two components are joined together by a thin wire.

10. This is a very unique form of artwork.

11. The other alternative choice is to ask for their help.

12. When we combined our collections together, there were more than six thousand stamps for display.

13. Unlike the old buildings, the new block is rectangular in shape.

14. The principal thinks that it is absolutely necessary for us to be punctual.

C. **Rewrite the following sentences by replacing the wordy phrase in each sentence with a more precise word.**

1. There will be a celebration prior to the time of the game.

   _____

2. They sailed along the river by means of a houseboat.

   _____

3. We are given to understand that the show will be postponed.

   _____

4. There was little precipitation in the month of May.

   _____

5. In spite of the fact that we made a profit, he did not consider this deal a worthwhile one.

   _____

D. Read the following passage. Underline the superfluous words or phrases. Rewrite them in a more concise way.

Thousands of years ago, people already knew how to make hot air balloons that could rise up into the air. In China, unmanned hot air balloons without passengers, called Kongming lanterns, were reportedly used for military signalling in the Three Kingdoms era.

Some people also believe that hot air balloons were believed to be used by the Nazca Indians of Peru some 1500 years ago as a tool for designing vast drawings on the Nazca plain.

The first hot air balloon capable of carrying passengers were built by the brothers Josef and Etienne Montgolfier in France. They were from a family of paper manufacturers. The reason why they managed to invent the hot air balloon was because they had noticed the ash rising in fires. Due to the fact that they had been successful with unmanned balloons, they started to experiment with flights that carried animals. The first balloon flight with human beings on board took place on the date of October 19, 1783. The first hot air balloons were basically cloth bags with a smoky fire on a grill attached to the bottom. They could catch fire easily and be destroyed upon landing on the ground.

Hot air balloons are able to fly above the ground to extremely high altitudes in the sky. The highest hot air balloon flight reached an altitude of 21 290 metres. The furthest that a hot air balloon managed to fly was a distance of 7671.91 kilometres. The longest duration that a hot air balloon flight ever made was 50 hours and 38 minutes.

Today, hot air balloons are used primarily for recreation. As a matter of fact, there are some 7000 hot air balloons operating in the United States.

_____

_____

_____

_____

_____

_____

_____

_____

_____

_____

_____

_____

_____

_____

_____

_____

_____

Clauses

Clauses are the smaller sentences that are linked (by words such as "and", "but", "because", "when", etc.) to form a larger sentence. A clause has the same structure as a sentence but it is part of a larger sentence.

Examples: *She has been playing the violin for some years <u>but</u> she's not good at it.*

He was furious <u>because</u> someone broke his antique vase.

They were dancing happily <u>when</u> he arrived.

A. **Identify the smaller sentences (clauses) in each of the following sentences. Write them on the lines provided.**

1. I didn't lose my temper although I was really mad at her.

   _____

   _____

2. The game was tough but we managed to score in the third quarter.

   _____

   _____

3. They made me captain because I was the tallest among them.

   _____

   _____

4. Unless you invite her in person, she won't be coming.

   _____

   _____

5. When I opened the closet door, a mouse darted out.

   _____

   _____

6. The weather turned bad and we ended up playing chess at John's home.

   _____

   _____

Types of Clauses

Clauses that are linked by conjunctions such as "**and**" and "**but**" are called **coordinate clauses**. They function as equal partners in a sentence.

Example: *He introduced me to Karmel* and *we shook hands*.

Clauses that depend on other clauses to complete the meaning are called **subordinate clauses**.

Example: *Whatever you do*, you'll have my support.

Clauses that subordinate clauses depend on are called **main clauses**.

Example: Whatever you do, *you'll have my support*.

B. Read the following paragraph about Jackie Robinson. Give one example for each type of clause learned.

Jackie Robinson attended Pasadena Junior College where he set records in track and field, quarterbacked the football team, and led the basketball team in scoring. As a shortstop on the Pasadena varsity baseball team, Jackie led the team to the championship and was voted MVP. After two years at Pasadena College, Jackie graduated and he was offered numerous scholarships to major universities. He chose UCLA where he became an athletic hero.

Coordinate Clause

_____

_____

Subordinate Clause

_____

_____

Main Clause

_____

_____

C. **Add a subordinate clause or a main clause to complete each of the following sentences.**

1. _____
   because we didn't expect it.

2. _____
   when the teacher called her.

3. _____ ,
   they will go anyway.

4. _____ ,
   they ended up losing.

5. _____ ,
   he will let you know.

6. Although it was raining heavily, _____
   _____

7. Unless you let me know in advance, _____
   _____

8. Since there was no electricity, _____
   _____

9. While the girls were busy preparing for the party, _____
   _____

10. Despite the fact that he missed the deadline, _____
    _____

11. If he picked the red one, _____
    _____

12. Even if _____ ,
    they will hold the meeting.

D. **Using what you have learned about main clauses, subordinate clauses, and coordinate clauses, combine the following small sentences to form larger sentences. Make any necessary changes.**

1. The guests arrived. Mr. and Mrs. Lyman were busy setting the table. The children were tidying up the living room.

   _____

   _____

2. We were down by three at the bottom of the seventh inning. We had confidence in winning the game.

   _____

   _____

3. The wind subsided. They were thinking of setting out again.

   _____

   _____

4. You pay in full. You will get one month's service free. You will receive an accessory of your choice.

   _____

   _____

5. You may take the red binder. You may take the blue binder. You cannot take both binders.

   _____

   _____

6. I sought Ray's help. He knew the way to the cave.

   _____

   _____

   _____

   _____

14 More on Clauses

Relative Clauses

A **relative clause** refers to a subordinate clause that helps identify someone or something by providing information about them.

Example: *Robert is a new student.*
Robert, <u>who sits next to Emily</u>, is a new student.

A.   Identify and underline the relative clause in each of the following sentences.

1.   The batter was using a bat that was way too long for him.

2.   That is the building where Uncle Jeff used to work.

3.   Dr. Martin, who turned 50 last week, has been our family doctor for 10 years.

4.   The tie that Paul was wearing actually belongs to me.

5.   The video game which was released yesterday is sold out.

6.   Mrs. Walsh, whom everybody likes, is leaving the school in June.

B.   Join each pair of sentences by turning one into a relative clause.

1.   He was wearing a T-shirt. It didn't fit him.

   _____

   _____

2.   This is the place. Mabel was telling us about the place.

   _____

3.   The team was determined to come back big. The team had lost five games in a row.

   _____

   _____

4. My father will visit Brazil next week. My father has never been to any countries in South America.

5. The library has a wide collection of storybooks. Pam's mother works in the library.

6. Mr. Foster has just finished writing a book. The book is about developing a winning attitude.

C. Add a relative clause to each of the following sentences.

1. The office has been reconfigured.

2. The trip will take more than a week.

3. She picked a dress.

4. The figure skater fell accidentally.

5. Jodie will celebrate her 13th birthday this Saturday.

6. The visitor is interested in the models we made.

14 More on Clauses

Noun Clauses and Adverb Clauses

A **noun clause** functions like a noun in a sentence.

Examples: <u>What you've told the police</u> is crucial to solving the case.
(functions as a subject)

I understand <u>that he will not be able to make it today</u>.
(functions as an object)

An **adverb clause** functions like an adverbial in the main clause of a sentence.

Examples: Please put the documents <u>where they were supposed to be</u>.
(location)

Tell me <u>when you are ready</u>.
(time)

D. **Decide whether the underlined clauses are noun clauses or adverb clauses. Write "N" for noun clauses and "ADV" for adverb clauses.**

1. <u>If we don't hurry</u>, we'll be late for the train. _____

2. The ceremony will begin <u>when the guest of honour arrives</u>. _____

3. <u>Who speaks first</u> doesn't matter that much. _____

4. The teacher did not know <u>if he really understood what she had told him</u>. _____

5. Let me know <u>what you think about the proposal by tomorrow</u>. _____

6. The children had to stay in the room <u>until their mothers came to pick them up</u>. _____

7. He was told to say <u>whatever was in his mind</u>. _____

8. <u>Whoever has the access card</u> can enter the premises of the institution. _____

9. They ate and ate <u>as if they had been starving for weeks</u>! _____

140

E. Expand each of the following sentences by adding a noun clause or an adverb clause.

1. He was driving (how).

    _____

2. The new building stood (where).

    _____

3. You should remember (something).

    _____

4. I'll give it to you (on what condition).

    _____

5. They were shut out (why).

    _____

6. I was just told (something).

    _____

7. We can have a game of soccer (when).

    _____

    _____

8. The police seemed to know (something).

    _____

    _____

9. (The matter) did not affect her in any way.

    _____

    _____

10. The firefighter managed to rescue him (when).

    _____

    _____

15 More on Relative Clauses

Relative Clauses

Relative clauses are also called **adjectival clauses** since they identify or describe nouns, just like adjectives do.

Examples: *Visitors <u>who hold a valid ticket</u> are entitled to a souvenir pack.*
(identifies the visitors)

That is an idea <u>that only he can think of</u>.
(describes the idea)

We use a relative pronoun (that, which, who, whom, whose) or a relative adverb (where, when, why) to link a relative clause to the part of the sentence it describes.

A. **Fill in the blanks with the appropriate relative pronouns or relative adverbs.**

1. The man _____ Betsy chatted with is one of the volunteers.

2. May I know the reason _____ you left early?

3. He knows someone _____ works as a game developer.

4. The students _____ parents are at work can stay behind and join the after-school program.

5. I think I've found a way _____ will solve your problem.

6. The story _____ Mr. Watson mentioned was written by Dan Dawson.

7. Samantha is a girl _____ wants everything her way.

8. We will meet in the room _____ all the tools are kept.

9. I don't remember the occasion _____ we met for the first time.

10. The car _____ he is showing us belongs to his brother.

Omitting Relative Pronouns

Generally the **relative pronouns** "who", "whom", "which", and "that" can be omitted.

Example: *The man <u>that</u> I just mentioned is standing right over there.*

The man I just mentioned is standing right over there.

However, if they are the subject of the clause, they cannot be omitted.

Example: *Was she the one <u>who</u> had been accused of stealing the money?*

B. Decide if the relative pronouns in the following sentences can be omitted. Cross out the ones that can be omitted.

1. Is this the book that you lent me last week?

2. I don't recall having met a girl who auditioned with you.

3. The puppy that she gave me has gained quite a bit of weight.

4. The teacher whose son is in our class is called Mr. Layton.

5. Who was the dancer that played the little swan in last night's show?

6. The story which I've just read is about an elf living in a jungle.

7. The team that we are going to play against is on a seven-game winning streak.

C. Combine each pair of sentences without using relative pronouns.

1. The boy is called Simon. I talked to Simon just now.

   _____

2. Alice is wearing the dress. Alice's mother made the dress for her.

   _____

3. I like the nifty MP3 player. My brother gave me the MP3 player.

   _____

4. The members don't support the plan. Ron proposed the plan.

   _____

15 More on Relative Clauses

Defining and Non-defining Relative Clauses

Defining relative clauses identify or describe a particular person or thing.

Non-defining relative clauses merely provide additional information about a person or thing.

Examples: Mrs. Green, <u>who taught us History last year</u>, will retire this summer.
(non-defining because it merely adds information about Mrs. Green)

The teacher <u>who taught us History last year</u> will retire this summer.
(defining because it identifies a person)

A non-defining relative clause is separated from the main sentence by commas.

D. Compare each of the following pairs of sentences. Decide whether the relative clauses are defining or non-defining. Write "D" for defining and "N" for non-defining.

1. a. Yesterday on my way home, I met Mr. Jenkins, who asked me about Tim. _____

    b. Yesterday on my way home, I met a man who asked me about Tim. _____

2. a. My brother broke the watch that I had given him for his birthday. _____

    b. My brother broke his watch, which I had given him for his birthday. _____

3. a. I find the story that Bill told me hard to believe. _____

    b. We all enjoyed the story, which ended on a happy note. _____

4. a. The pitcher who shut out the opposing team is in fact a rookie. _____

    b. The pitcher, who shut out the opposing team, is a contending Cy Young winner. _____

5. a. She is the dancer that mesmerized the audience with her spectacular performance. _____

    b. The dancer, who mesmerized the audience with her spectacular performance, will leave the troupe soon. _____

E. Complete each of the following sentences with a non-defining relative clause.

1. I spoke to the school librarian, _____
_____

2. Sitting over there is Mr. Johnson, _____
_____

3. The children listened attentively to their teacher, _____
_____

4. She will leave with Jerry, _____
_____

5. Carrie waited for her school principal, _____
_____

F. Complete each of the following sentences with a defining relative clause.

1. A cat _____
_____

2. If you happen to come across a man _____
_____

3. She is the one _____
_____

4. This morning I saw a car _____
_____

5. An archaeologist is someone _____
_____

6. Nina gave me a book _____
_____

16 Types of Sentences

Sentences

There are four types of **sentences**.

1. **Simple sentence**: consisting of one single clause
2. **Compound sentence**: made up of two or more coordinate clauses
3. **Complex sentence**: made up of one main clause and one or more subordinate clauses
4. **Compound-complex sentence**: made up of two or more coordinate main clauses along with one or more subordinate clauses

---

A. **Read the following sentences. Write "S" for simple sentences, "CP" for compound sentences, "CX" for complex sentences, and "CPX" for compound-complex sentences.**

1. I was taken aback by her candid remarks. _____

2. Julie didn't want to spoil the fun and so she stayed mum. _____

3. After the postman had delivered the parcel, they started guessing whom it was from. _____

4. As a matter of fact, the two cylinders are not identical. _____

5. Wherever I go, I always see Sam's little poodle. _____

6. At the bottom of the ninth inning, Matt hit a walk-away homerun. _____

7. No matter what he does, his mother always says that it's not good enough and asks him to do it better next time. _____

8. The night sky was clear and we could see many twinkling stars. _____

9. If you happen to see Tim, please tell him to see Mrs. Corr right away or he can leave a note for her if he can't find her in her room. _____

10. We can stay put at that motel or we can move on but we must decide now. _____

B. Underline the compound sentences in the following paragraph. Change them into complex sentences. Write them on the lines provided.

If we have to describe pizza to someone who has never seen or eaten it before, how can we go about doing it? Here is Sandy's attempt: "Pizza is an oven-baked, flat, round bread and it is covered with tomato sauce and toppings. There is a wide variety of toppings to choose from for your pizza. Pepperoni, bell peppers, ham, and mushrooms are the most common toppings. The crust of a pizza is plain, but some people prefer to season it with butter, garlic, herbs, or cheese. In Canada, we have our own "Canadian pizza" and this kind of pizza has the topping combination of back bacon, pepperoni, and mushrooms. In Quebec, however, the same topping combination is called a "Québécois Pizza".

_____

_____

_____

_____

_____

_____

_____

_____

C. **Rewrite the following lengthy sentences. Use simple sentences to replace some of the clauses.**

1. While they were waiting to be rescued, which seemed to be less and less likely to come by, they tried to see if they could salvage anything nearby that could keep them warm, as the temperature seemed to be dropping, which made survival even harder.

   _____

   _____

   _____

   _____

2. Although they were down by two, the players did not lose heart because they believed that there was still time to catch up and as long as they could mount an all-out offence and did not let up, they could crack open the opponents' line of defence, which showed signs of fatigue.

   _____

   _____

   _____

   _____

3. Although true seals are more streamlined than fur seals and can swim more effectively over long distances, they are clumsier on land because unlike fur seals, they cannot turn their hind flippers downward, which forces them to wriggle with their front flippers and abdominal muscles.

   _____

   _____

   _____

   _____

D. Develop a compound sentence and then a complex or compound-complex sentence based on each of the following simple sentences.

1. They were happy.

    _____

    _____

    _____

2. No one said a word.

    _____

    _____

    _____

3. The show was over.

    _____

    _____

    _____

4. We must set off.

    _____

    _____

    _____

5. They were expecting some good news.

    _____

    _____

    _____

Review 2

A. Read the clues and fill in the missing letters to spell these words.

1. someone in times of joy and grief   f _ _ _ _ _ _

2. full of excessive pride   c _ n _ _ _ _ _

3. planning the amount of money to spend   b _ d _ _ _ _ _

4. heaviness   w _ _ _ _ _

5. often found in a harbour   p _ _ _

6. bird with a habit of hoarding bright objects   m _ g p _ _

7. start   b _ g _ _

8. inhaling and exhaling   b _ _ _ _ _ _ _

B. Identify the underlined phrases. Write "NP" for noun phrases, "VP" for verb phrases, and "PP" for prepositional phrases.

1. "There's <u>a new painting</u> on the wall, don't you see?" Gail asks.   _____

2. Alan <u>will be taking off</u> for his trip early tomorrow.   _____

3. "Do you wish to go <u>beyond your limits</u>?" asks Megan's coach.   _____

4. My brother composed a memorable song about <u>a weeping camel</u>.   _____

5. The story is about a kingdom <u>on the mountain</u> and the valley folk below.   _____

6. Wendy says her collage is <u>a mix of original drawings and photographs</u>.   _____

7. "Do it <u>in the name of heaven</u>!" exclaims Bob's character.   _____

8. Vicky is giggling because her cat <u>is chasing</u> a rolling ball of yarn.   _____

9. "No matter how much you practise the piano, your chubby fingers <u>are not going to grow</u>!" mischievous Ben says to his sister.   _____

10. Isn't it amazing that some stand-up comics can imitate <u>all sorts of accents</u>?   _____

C. Read the following paragraph and identify the underlined phrases. Write them on the lines.

The human voice is a beautiful musical instrument. It is complex, too, falling into different types: <u>a male voice</u> can be a bass, a baritone, or a tenor; a female voice can be an alto, a mezzo-soprano, or a soprano. If you are lucky, you <u>will even find</u> a rare counter tenor (an <u>adult male alto</u> voice) or a contralto (the lowest female singing voice). Each voice type produces a distinctive character, called "timbre", varying from being <u>full and rich</u> to being <u>sweet and lyrical</u>. You <u>may have heard</u> that some singers are "dark" while others are "bright" – the former is associated with <u>lower-pitched</u> voice types, the latter with higher-pitched voices. Some people sing <u>really well</u> at a young age, but it actually takes a long time to polish the singing voice; a singer must <u>very patiently</u> train <u>to "master the instrument"</u>. When polished voices come together <u>to perform a colourful song</u>, the music can blow you away! The next time you are at a choral performance, try to listen for <u>the different shades of sound</u>. You may be surprised by how much you hear!

1. Noun Phrases: _____

_____

2. Verb Phrases: _____

_____

3. Adjective Phrases: _____

_____

4. Adjectival Phrases: _____

_____

5. Adverb Phrases: _____

_____

6. Adverbial Phrases: _____

_____

D. Cross out the superfluous words or phrases in these sentences.

1. It is most definitely true that milk is good for you.

2. In my opinion, I believe that everyone deserves to live in a free country.

3. Could you repeat the question one more time, please?

4. This dictionary is so massively heavy that you can use it to do weightlifting.

5. Gordon's personal view is that the tree should not be cut down.

6. See? I have told you many times already before that this is a bad idea.

7. Whenever my sister is out of things to do in her spare time, she reads.

8. You would not believe how terribly horrible this movie is!

9. Mary's piece of work is more unique than Paul's.

E. Match the underlined adverb clauses with the uses. Write the letters.

A. Andrea will go <u>wherever life takes her</u>.

B. We stayed around a bit <u>after you left the party</u>.

C. I picked up the newspaper already <u>since you were still sleeping</u>.

D. Sue brought a book along <u>so that she would have something to read</u>.

E. <u>If only I had followed my grandmother's advice</u>, I would never have got myself into trouble.

F. "<u>Even though I hate vegetable sticks</u>, I will eat some at your birthday party," says my little cousin.

1. Adverb Clause of Time _____ 2. Adverb Clause of Place _____

3. Adverb Clause of Reason _____ 4. Adverb Clause of Purpose _____

5. Adverb Clause of Contrast _____ 6. Adverb Clause of Condition _____

F. Underline the smaller sentences in each of the following. Then write the conjunction.

1. The script is superb but the acting is lousy. _____

2. Mike is still in touch with Neal even though they live far from each other. _____

3. Jake will stay in the neighbourhood as long as his cousin is around.

_____

4. This sauce is delicious because Mom put in a lot of garlic and onions.

_____

5. The bugs scurried away when we switched on the lights!

_____

6. Amanda will not leave her room until she has cleaned it inside out.

_____

7. Come to Halifax to visit me or go to Charlottetown to visit Jen.

_____

G. Read the following paragraph and underline the subordinate clauses.

Alsace is one of the 26 regions of France, bordering Germany and Switzerland. Although it is part of France, it has changed hands between France and Germany many times, which is why its architecture, language, cuisine, music, dress, and even economy have a unique mixture of French and German traditions. As it is a region with a semi-continental climate, Alsace has cold, dry winters and hot summers. You may want to visit Alsace if you are a tree lover, because it contains many forests. The region may also interest you if you are a lover of history, since it was once part of the Holy Roman Empire and is still inhabited by people who speak a dialect of Upper German.

H. Read each sentence and cross out the relative pronoun if it can be omitted.

1. Is this the movie that you have always wanted to see?

2. Let me introduce you to the teacher who taught me how to sing.

3. Why don't we go to the restaurant that is around the corner?

4. I am reading the book which you gave me a year ago.

5. That is the dog whose owner lives two houses from Sam.

6. The place that you are going to is where Sara grew up.

7. When is Tom going to tell me the story that he told you?

8. The performer whom you were pointing out to me is actually my sister!

I. Complete each sentence by adding a noun clause or an adverb clause.

1. Felicity said (something).

    _____

2. The curtain will rise (when).

    _____

3. Let Mr. Stevenson know (something).

    _____

4. We will play our baseball game (where).

    _____

5. My friend was very upset (why).

    _____

6. Uncle Bill will only cook (on what condition).

    _____

7. (The matter) will not change her mind.

    _____

8. Alex was talking (how).

    _____

J. **Read each sentence and decide whether the relative clause is defining (D) or non-defining (N). Then write a sentence with each type of clause.**

1. a. In my dream, Henry and I were playing in a room, which is the one in our old house. _____

   b. In my dream, Henry and I were playing in the room that was left empty. _____

2. a. The teacher who conducts our school band is retiring this year. _____

   b. Our grade seven teacher, who is also the music teacher, is retiring this year. _____

3. a. The speed skater that my brother drew in class has won the gold medal this year! _____

   b. My brother's favourite speed skater, whom he drew in class, has just won the gold medal! _____

4. a. _____

   _____

   b. _____

   _____

K. **Rewrite this lengthy sentence. You may need to change the order of ideas.**

He has heard from his friends that this movie, which has a well-written script and stunning visual effects, will take his breath away, even though he generally does not like movies because they always put him to sleep, which is something he already does ten hours a day.

_____

_____

_____

_____

_____

Section 3

Usage

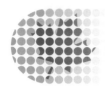

1 Creating Images with Words

Creating Images

In writing, we use precise words to create vivid **images** to arouse our readers' interest and imagination.

Examples:

General Word	Precise Word	Image
house	mansion	big, impressive
	hut	small, crude
hit	slap	hit with palm
	jab	sharp punch

A. Think of three precise words for each of the following "general" words.

1. walk _____ _____ _____

2. eat _____ _____ _____

3. car _____ _____ _____

4. cold _____ _____ _____

5. hot _____ _____ _____

6. kind _____ _____ _____

7. poor _____ _____ _____

8. rich _____ _____ _____

9. quick _____ _____ _____

10. building _____ _____ _____

B. Rewrite the following paragraph, replacing the general words with precise words.

Our farm was about 30 kilometres from the closest town. It was big and beautiful. Life on the farm was simple. We followed the same routine, day in and day out. I helped feed the animals and do household chores. In my leisure, I used to ride a horse and go around the vicinity. There was a small river where my friends and I liked going. There was a lot to see in summer: insects, birds, trees, frogs, and little animals. In winter, it was a totally different picture. Everything seemed to come to a halt. The brook was frozen and there were few living things in sight.

_____

_____

_____

_____

_____

_____

_____

_____

_____

_____

_____

_____

_____

_____

_____

Similes and Metaphors

A **simile** is a comparison of two things using "as" or "like".

Examples: The little boy swam <u>like a fish</u>.

Swift as lightning, the eagle grabbed the salmon and soared into the air.

A **metaphor** is a comparison of two unlike things to create a common idea.

Examples: Her life is <u>a tragic show</u>.

The sun <u>soothes and kisses</u> the flowers.

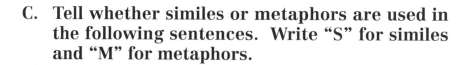

C. Tell whether similes or metaphors are used in the following sentences. Write "S" for similes and "M" for metaphors.

1. Grandfather slept like a log. _____

2. Like a bulldozer, he was determined to overcome all the obstacles. _____

3. To her, life is a kaleidoscope. _____

4. Stubborn as a rock, he refused to budge. _____

5. The parched land drank every single drop of rain. _____

6. The breeze was humming a lullaby and soon the baby was asleep. _____

7. The news knocked him off guard. _____

8. The crowd dispersed like ants. _____

D. Add a simile to each of the following sentences. Your simile can be a single word or a phrase. Add articles if necessary.

1. He gazed at me like _____

2. The day was as hot as _____

3. The team was as fierce as _____

4. The truck rolled over like _____

5. He is as sneaky as _____

6. We all find him as funny as _____

7. The little boy was running around like _____

8. The man had spiky hair like _____

E. Write about the following, using metaphors.

1. a skyscraper

_____

2. a courageous firefighter

_____

3. a speeding car

_____

4. the passage of time

_____

5. the chilly weather

_____

6. a losing team in the hope of a comeback

_____

7. some soothing music

_____

8. a long and winding road

_____

2 Writing at the Sentence Level

Simple sentences are easy to understand but too many simple sentences make our writing choppy and affect coherence. In writing, we should vary the construction of sentences for a more interesting reading experience.

Inverting Word Order

Inverting the order of words in a sentence can create an interesting presentation of ideas.

Example: *The eagle soared high in the clear blue sky.*

High in the clear blue sky, the eagle soared.

A. Rewrite each of the following sentences by inverting the word order. Make any other necessary changes.

1. He lay there for hours without making any sound.

   _____

2. The geese flew in the V-formation across the sky.

   _____

3. A dark, shadowy thing was slithering in the murky water.

   _____

4. The game, well into the last quarter, was exciting as ever.

   _____

5. They trudged along, against the strong wind and scattered showers.

   _____

   _____

6. The audience applauded excitedly, awed by the pianist's superb performance.

   _____

   _____

B. Read the following paragraphs and rewrite the underlined sentences by inverting the word order. Make any necessary changes.

1. <u>My hobby is collecting stamps.</u> It all started when I was six. We got a letter from Uncle Lyman. 2. <u>There was a beautiful stamp on the envelope.</u> It was the picture of a robin. Mom let me keep it. And that was the first stamp of my collection. To date, I have collected more than five hundred stamps from various places and countries. 3. <u>I get to know many exotic and faraway places through stamp collecting.</u>

4. <u>Now it seems to be more and more difficult to get stamps.</u> People prefer sending e-mail. 5. <u>Another favourite way of communication is instant messaging.</u> Who would send letters when communication has become so instantaneous?

In fact, letters are now nicknamed "snail mail". So we end up receiving fewer and fewer letters. Someday, stamps will not be needed anymore. 6. <u>They will disappear, just like dinosaurs.</u> And my stamps will become antique!

1. _____

2. _____

_____

3. _____

_____

4. _____

_____

5. _____

_____

6. _____

Using Phrases to Begin Sentences

Using **prepositional** and **infinitive phrases**, and **verbals** to begin sentences are effective ways to vary the construction of sentences.

Examples: One must be over 12 to be qualified for the race.
               To be qualified for the race, one must be over 12. *(infinitive phrase)*

               We strolled leisurely with our Labrador along the river bank.
               Along the river bank, we strolled leisurely with our Labrador. *(prepositional phrase)*

               His daily workout is jogging for five kilometres.
               Jogging for five kilometres is his daily workout. *(gerund)*

C. **Rewrite each of the following sentences by varying its structure. Make any necessary changes but maintain its meaning.**

1. The bridegroom waited patiently for the bride in front of the altar.

   _____

   _____

2. I think we need an additional component to make this device work.

   _____

   _____

3. What he needs most are exercising and getting plenty of rest.

   _____

   _____

4. Their boat sailed slowly down the meandering river.

   _____

   _____

5. The two groups wanted to get through the hurdle and they decided to join forces.

   _____

   _____

Adding Details to Sentences

We can make sentences more interesting and informative by **adding details**.

Example: I heard a sound.

I heard a <u>faint</u> sound, which was <u>like a droplet landing on the floor</u>.

D. Make three new sentences by expanding each of the following sentences. Add details to make the new sentences different from the original and from one another.

1. They were excited.

   a. _____

   b. _____

   c. _____

2. The meeting ended.

   a. _____

   b. _____

   c. _____

3. We watched the game.

   a. _____

   b. _____

   c. _____

4. The children laughed.

   a. _____

   b. _____

   c. _____

3 Combining Simple Sentences

Although lengthy sentences can make our writing complicated to follow, too many simple sentences would give our writing an unstylish feel. This is especially so when we use too many verbs that don't show any action.

We can combine simple sentences into more compact sentences by using:

- appositives,
- compound sentences,
- subordinate clauses, and
- participle phrases.

Using Appositives

An **appositive** is renaming or re-identifying something mentioned earlier in the text. Often, we need a pair of commas to set it off from the rest of the sentence.

Example: *Ted is my best friend. He is the youngest in his family.*

                    Ted, my best friend, is the youngest in his family.

     or   *My best friend, Ted, is the youngest in his family.*

A. Use appositives to make compact sentences.

1. Raymond is my teacher's son. He often stays behind to help me with math.

2. The Eiffel Tower is one of the most famous structures in the world. It welcomes six million visitors every year.

3. We used to have lunch at the Wok. It was a family restaurant famous for its fried rice.

4. My cousin was involved in designing the overpass system. He is a civil engineer.

5. The castle is the landmark of the city. It overlooks the entire harbour.

B. Combine the following simple sentences into compound sentences and complex sentences.

1. He reached the theatre at about eight. Macy was nowhere to be found.

   Compound _____

   Complex _____

2. Keep up the fighting spirit. We still have a chance to avoid being eliminated.

   Compound _____

   Complex _____

3. The snowstorm is on its way. It will take a day or two to reach this part of the province.

   Compound _____

   _____

   Complex _____

   _____

4. We did not expect him to arrive a day earlier than scheduled. The set-up was therefore not ready yet.

   Compound _____

   _____

   Complex _____

   _____

5. Let me have more data. Then I will be able to provide you with a more accurate assessment.

   Compound _____

   _____

   Complex _____

   _____

Using Participle Phrases to Connect Ideas

We can integrate the idea of one sentence into a larger structure by turning that idea into a **participle phrase**.

Example: *The guests gathered at the hall. They were waiting for the mayor to arrive.*

Gathering at the hall, the guests were waiting for the mayor to arrive.

C.   Join the following pairs of sentences using participle phrases.

1.   They sailed along the river. They hoped to reach the town in two hours.

   _____

2.   The students waited anxiously in the classroom. They wanted to know the results first-hand.

   _____

3.   We had played for more than an hour. We were getting tired and decided to go home.

   _____

4.   He drove on slowly. He looked for the sign that pointed him to Townsville.

   _____

5.   The children were still arguing about who to start first. They did not realize that there was only one minute left.

   _____

6.   The mayor spoke to the audience. He reiterated the importance of going green.

   _____

7.   He noticed that it was getting late. He decided to put up for the night at a nearby motel.

   _____

8.   The crowd wanted to find out what had happened. They moved closer to the collapsed house.

   _____

D. Rewrite the following paragraph in a more compact way. You may use all or any of the ways you have learned in combining simple sentences.

How would you feel if you had a chance to skate 57 metres above Paris? How would you do that? A real skaters' ramp is installed on the first level of the Eiffel Tower. It measures 15 m by 7.5 m. The ramp overlooks the Champ de Mars. It gives skaters a spectacular view. You can reach the ramp by the elevators or the stairs. You can warm up by taking the stairs. There are a total of 345 steps leading to the ramp. Unfortunately, the ramp will be there for just three days each year in winter. During the three days, there will be licensed skaters on hand. They will assist people of all ages in learning to skate.

_____

_____

_____

_____

_____

_____

_____

_____

_____

_____

_____

_____

_____

4 Paragraphing

> A **paragraph** is a thought unit within a piece of writing. Sentences gather words and phrases into units of meaning; these sentences, in turn, are gathered into paragraphs. Since paragraphs help the reader see important thought units, we should start a new paragraph whenever we begin writing about a new organizational topic.

A. Read the following text and decide where to break it into paragraphs. Put // to indicate the beginning of a new paragraph.

Drinking tea has been associated with health benefits for centuries, but it is only in recent years that its medicinal properties have been investigated scientifically and proven. Tea's health benefits are largely due to its high content of catechins. Green tea is the best source of catechins. Catechins are more powerful than vitamins C and E in preventing oxidation from damaging cells. They appear to have other disease-fighting properties too. In fact, studies have found that consuming green tea can reduce risks of cancer. Regular consumption of green and black teas also helps reduce risks of heart disease. The antioxidants in green, black, and oolong teas can help block the oxidation of LDL (bad) cholesterol, increase HDL (good) cholesterol, and improve artery function. To get the most out of tea drinking, we should drink a cup of tea a few times a day to absorb antioxidants and other healthful plant compounds. The usual amount is three cups per day. Also, we should allow tea to steep for three to five minutes to bring out its catechins, and the best way to get the catechins in tea is to drink it freshly brewed. Tea can impede the absorption of iron from fruits and vegetables, but adding lemon or milk will counteract this problem.

Number of Paragraphs

In general, we start a new paragraph whenever we begin writing about a new cluster of ideas. At times, however, we may find that two or three minor points can be treated in a single paragraph, or we may discover that what appeared at first like a minor point can be expanded to become more than one paragraph.

B. Read the following sentences about tea drinking. They are already arranged in sequence. Try grouping them into two or three paragraphs.

It is believed that tea drinking originated from China.

It was the second emperor of China, Shen Nung, who discovered tea.

One day, Emperor Shen Nung was sipping a cup of hot water in his garden when a tea leaf dropped into his cup.

He liked the flavour of the water with the leaf in it, and from then onward, he put tea leaves in the hot water he drank.

Soon, his people followed suit and put tea leaves in hot water.

Tea drinking became more and more popular.

Some even added onion, ginger, or spices to make medicinal beverages.

_____

_____

_____

_____

_____

_____

_____

_____

C. **Read the following jumbled sentences. Arrange them in order and group them into paragraphs. Write the paragraphs in the space provided.**

In those days, lunch was served at noon but dinner was not eaten until late at night.

In fact, they are two entirely different things.

Afternoon tea began in the mid-1800s.

A noblewoman, the Duchess of Bedford, found herself hungry during those long afternoon hours and so she started having a tray of tea with bread and butter served to her in the mid-afternoon.

Most people think that afternoon tea is synonymous with high tea.

And although high tea sounds classy, it actually consisted of a full dinner for the common people.

Soon, she began to invite other ladies to join her.

High tea, on the other hand, was served around six in the evening.

Tea was still served, but there would also be meats, fish or eggs, cheese, bread and butter, and cake.

Without realizing it, the Duchess of Bedford was setting the trend of having afternoon tea for the upper-class women.

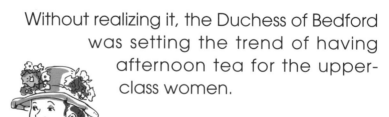

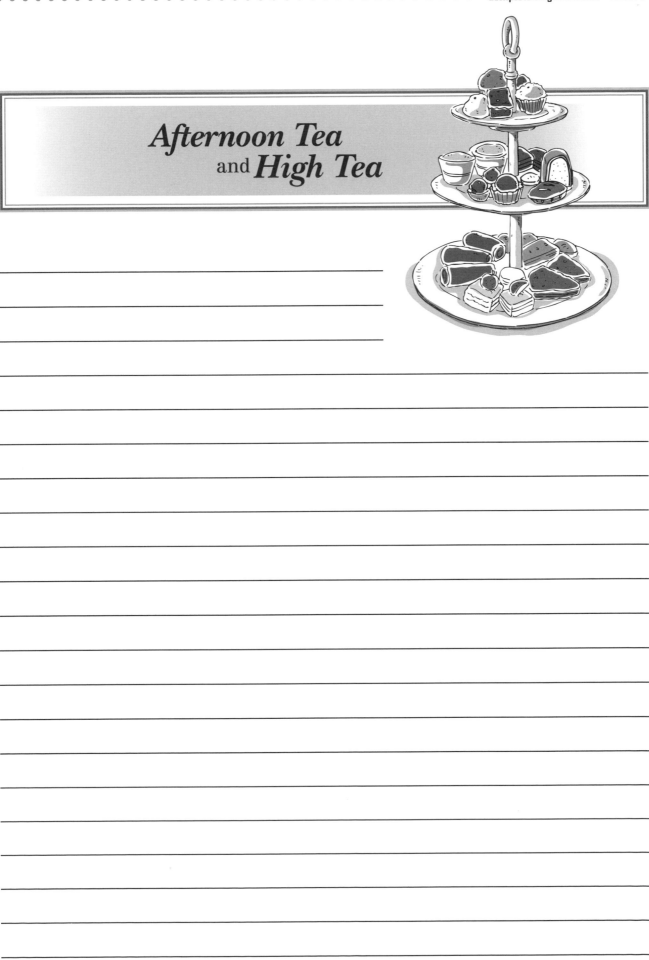

Afternoon Tea and High Tea

5 Building Paragraphs

A **paragraph** is usually made up of:

- a topic sentence (usually at the beginning)
- supporting sentences
- a closing sentence

Topic Sentence

It introduces the main idea of the paragraph and indicates to the reader what the paragraph will be about.

Supporting Sentences

They come after the topic sentence, making up the body of a paragraph. They also give details and examples to develop and support the main idea of the paragraph.

Closing Sentence

It is the last sentence in a paragraph. It restates the main idea in a different way or leads on to the next paragraph.

Example:

There are three reasons why the vice-president thinks Greg should be given the job. ← Topic sentence *First, Greg has the necessary skills. Second, he has the most relevant experience among the four* ← Supporting sentences *shortlisted candidates. In fact, he has handled six similar projects. Finally, she feels that Greg has the will to succeed.* *And I must say the* ← Closing sentence *last attribute is the most decisive.*

A. Write topic sentences for the following groups of supporting sentences.

1. _____
   _____
   _____

It is as large as a horse. In fact, the moose is the largest member of the deer family with long, dark brown hair, high, humped shoulders, and long legs. Each April, the male moose grows a set of antlers reaching 120 to 150 centimetres which he loses in the winter after rutting season.

2. _____
   _____
   _____

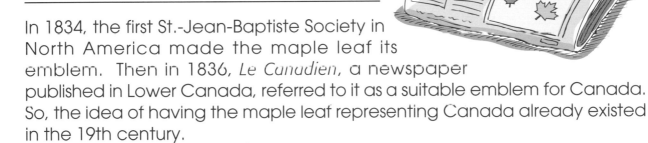

In 1834, the first St.-Jean-Baptiste Society in North America made the maple leaf its emblem. Then in 1836, *Le Canadien*, a newspaper published in Lower Canada, referred to it as a suitable emblem for Canada. So, the idea of having the maple leaf representing Canada already existed in the 19th century.

3. _____
   _____

Some people say that it all started when the English came to North America. They realized that they could move way faster on the ice-covered ponds than the grass, so they started playing ice hockey. Yet another guess at how hockey was invented is that the name "hockey" came from the French word "hocquet", meaning "Shepherd's Crook", which is the shape of a hockey stick. One thing is for sure, though – hockey has become a national sport in Canada.

B. Develop a topic sentence for each of the following topics that you are asked to write about.

1. Why people like keeping pets

   _____

   _____

   _____

2. Your favourite sport

   _____

   _____

   _____

3. An unforgettable experience

   _____

   _____

4. Your dream job

   _____

   _____

5. Recycle, reuse, and reduce

   _____

   _____

6. Music for therapy

   _____

   _____

7. What friends are for

   _____

   _____

C. **Choose two of the topic sentences you wrote in (B) and develop a paragraph for each by writing supporting details and a closing sentence.**

1. _____

_____

_____

_____

_____

_____

_____

_____

_____

_____

2. _____

_____

_____

_____

_____

_____

_____

_____

_____

_____

6 Taking Notes

We often make notes on something that we will write about later. The following guidelines may be helpful:

- Jot down only the main points and important information.
- Eliminate small connecting words.
- Eliminate pronouns.
- Don't eliminate these three words: and, in, on.
- Use symbols and abbreviations to save time.
- Organize notes in a logical sequence.

Common Symbols in Making Notes

+, &	plus, and, together with
=	equals
−	minus
#	number
X	times
>	greater than, more, larger
<	less than, smaller, fewer than
w/	with
w/o	without
w/in	within
→	leads to, produces, results in
←	from

A. Your teacher is explaining the proper way to read. Make notes on what she is telling you.

"Ask yourself if this has happened to you: you read an article or a chapter and soon afterwards, you are unable to recall much about it. Academic reading is different from reading for pleasure, like reading a paperback while on your way home. Many students don't see the difference between the two. They try to read a textbook as if it were a novel. Academic reading, I must say, requires different strategies.

Most students tend to skip the preface. Don't! You should read the preface to understand the author's perspective. The preface usually provides information about the author's objective, the organization of the book, how the book is different from other similar titles, and the author's background and qualifications. Once you know the author's objective, it's easier to see relationships among the facts presented.

The introduction is another part you shouldn't skip because the introduction lays the foundation for the rest of the text in the form of an overview and background information that will make it easier to digest information in the following chapters.

Reading articles often requires more than one pass. It usually takes two, three, or even more readings to grasp difficult or complicated concepts. You should always preview the material to be read, skim the table of contents, preface, headings, and conclusions.

In early readings, take brief notes by adding brackets in margins or underlining minimally. Note pages where you might want to take formal notes. After reading, take more extensive notes. When reading and note taking are complete, re-read what you have jotted down, think about what you've read, and add more notes based on your reflections. Your goal is to have notes that capture the essence of your reading so that you don't have to go back and re-read."

your **Notes**

_____

_____

_____

_____

_____

_____

_____

_____

_____

_____

_____

_____

B. Read the following article about the Internet. Make notes as you read on the benefits and dangers of the Internet for children.

The Internet is a global network of computers connected by cable and satellite. When users are connected to the Internet, they can receive texts, images, video, and sound on their computer from computers anywhere in the world. Just as there is a book or magazine on every subject in local libraries, bookshops, or newsagents, so is there information on virtually every subject on the Internet.

The Internet provides children and adults alike with a world of exciting opportunities – educational games and programs, research information for school projects and business, real-time communication with people from all around the world, sharing resources and ideas with others, as well as online shopping.

The Internet uses multimedia and interactivity extensively. Using multimedia means that you can access not only written words, but also pictures, music, and sound effects. Interactivity means that users can choose what they want by the click of a mouse. The resources on the Internet are infinite; they entertain as well as educate.

There are, however, no regulations or controls on the material that is placed on the Internet. While there are millions of children's sites on the net, there are million others that are not suitable for children. Children can unexpectedly come across material of a sexual or violent nature, language that is rude, and the advertising of children's products. Quite innocently, they can bring up sites that do not relate to the topic they are looking for, or someone can send them images or messages that are not appropriate.

And as the search engines provide access to many sites on a given topic, even when children are searching for ordinary everyday topics, it is possible that they stumble across sites with information or images that could be harmful to them.

It is also possible that children will come into contact with people who are pretending to be children but have other motives. There is a real danger that children may come into contact with pedophiles or arrange to meet friends they have made online without really knowing who they are.

The Internet can become addictive, too. It is important that children do not use the Internet to the exclusion of other developmentally appropriate tasks, including the need to be physically active.

Your
Notes

7 Developing a Writing Plan

Planning is an important part of the writing process. It helps us organize our thoughts so that we can present them in a logical and systematic way. Below are some steps to follow in planning our writing:

1. Identify the topic.

2. Identify the type and purpose of writing.

3. Decide on the number of paragraphs.

4. Think about the topic sentences and supporting examples or descriptions for each paragraph.

5. Think about the opening and closing paragraphs. An opening paragraph introduces whereas a closing paragraph summarizes and concludes.

A. Choose the items that fit the writing task below.

Write an article for your school newsletter about a funny incident that happened to you and your friends at school.

1. The article should _____ .

   A. be entertaining   B. have a moral   C. not be long

2. Your target audience should probably be _____ .

   A. your schoolmates   B. your teachers   C. your parents

3. There should be at least _____ paragraphs.

   A. two   B. three   C. four

4. The first paragraph should best be used to _____ .

   A. create suspense   B. create a conflict   C. set the scene

5. The last paragraph should best be used to _____ .

   A. retell the story briefly

   B. tell what happened after the incident

   C. ask readers what might happen next

B. **Study each of the following topics and decide on the type and purpose of writing.**

1. *A Day in the Life of a Little Squirrel*

   Type and Purpose of Writing

   _____

   _____

   _____

2. *My Neighbourhood*

   Type and Purpose of Writing

   _____

   _____

   _____

3. *Sports Players as Role Models*

   Type and Purpose of Writing

   _____

   _____

   _____

4. *How to Live Green*

   Type and Purpose of Writing

   _____

   _____

   _____

C. **Choose one of the topics in (B) and develop a writing plan.**

Writing Plan

Topic: _____

Type and Purpose of Writing: _____

_____

Number of Paragraphs: _____

Topic Sentences:

1. Introduction: _____

_____

_____

2. Main Paragraphs:

A. _____

_____

_____

B. _____

_____

_____

> Number of main paragraphs varies.

C. _____

_____

3. Closing Paragraph: _____

_____

_____

D. Write about the topic you have chosen for (C), based on your writing plan.

8 Guiding Questions

Questions

Questions help us focus on the topic we want to write about. "Who", "what", "when", "where", "why", and "how" help us define the subject's scope and decide on the way in which we may want to approach the subject.

Example: <u>On Global Warming</u>

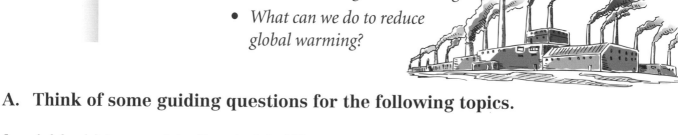

- *What is global warming?*
- *Why is there global warming?*
- *How serious is global warming?*
- *What can we do to reduce global warming?*

A. Think of some guiding questions for the following topics.

1. A Most Memorable Day in My Life

   _____

   _____

   _____

   _____

2. The Power of the Computer

   _____

   _____

   _____

   _____

3. My Favourite Sport

   _____

   _____

   _____

   _____

Developing Ideas

Questions also help us develop ideas. They force us to present our ideas in a logical sequence and an organized manner.

Example: _Topic Sentence_

Some people think that the sasquatch is only an imaginary creature while others believe that it really exists.

With the above topic sentence, we may immediately think of the following questions that would lead us to explore more about the topic sentence.

- What is the sasquatch?
- Where has it been sighted or found?
- Does the sasquatch really exist or is it more a folklore?
- How does the sasquatch look, according to those who claim to have seen one?
- Why do others think it is just a product of the imagination?

Based on the questions, we may develop the topic sentence into a paragraph as below:

The sasquatch is described as a large, hairy human-like creature living in remote forested areas of British Columbia.   ← What is the sasquatch?
← Where has it been sighted?

Over the years, there have been many reports of sightings of the sasquatch, with vivid descriptions and even evidence such as footprints and film footage.   ← How does the debate over whether the sasquatch is fact or fiction come about?

Descriptions of the sasquatch vary, but the creature is most often described as taller than a human, heavily built, and covered in long, thick, brown or black hair. It walks upright with a long stride.   ← What is the sasquatch like, according to eyewitnesses?

Most scientists, however, find that the physical evidence has been ambiguous at best, or hoaxes at worst. There have been no dead bodies, bones, or artifacts. And examinations of DNA samples indicate that they are from common animals.   ← Why do others think the sasquatch is fiction?

B. For each of the following topic sentences, list the questions you would ask yourself. Based on the questions, develop the topic sentence into a full paragraph.

1. Canada is a country that truly celebrates multiculturalism.

Questions

_____

_____

_____

_____

_____

_____

Paragraph

_____

_____

_____

_____

_____

_____

_____

_____

_____

2. English has become more like a global language.

Questions

_____

_____

_____

_____

_____

_____

_____

_____

_____

Paragraph

_____

_____

_____

_____

_____

_____

_____

_____

_____

_____

_____

9 Formal and Informal Writing

This is an **informal**, casual way of communicating with our friends and family that does not always follow precise rules of grammar. The sentence structure is quite casual, often involving the use of brief sentences or utterances.

Hi Angie, ← informal salutation

How are you? Hope all is well with you and your family. I'll be in town for a couple of days and — use of contraction

would like to pop in for a visit. — casual phrase

Call me or drop me an e-mail. Let's arrange a — casual phrase

get-together with Diane and Tricia. — use of contraction

Yours, ← casual closing

Beatrice

A. Rewrite the following sentences in an informal, casual way.

1. Please inform me of the date of your arrival so that I can meet you at the airport.

   _____

   _____

2. We shall meet to discuss the details and once we have decided a venue and the program, we will let you know.

   _____

   _____

3. Would you like to join me and my family on a trip to the cottage where we will plan to stay for the long weekend?

   _____

   _____

4. Since Teresa and Kitty will be staying at my place, I wonder if you would also like to join us so that the four of us could have some fun time together.

_____

_____

5. The coach informed us that the game would be postponed to Sunday and we would have one last practice on Friday afternoon at half past three sharp.

_____

_____

B. **Assume you are on holiday. Write an e-mail to your best friend or family telling them your experience. Maintain a casual tone in your writing.**

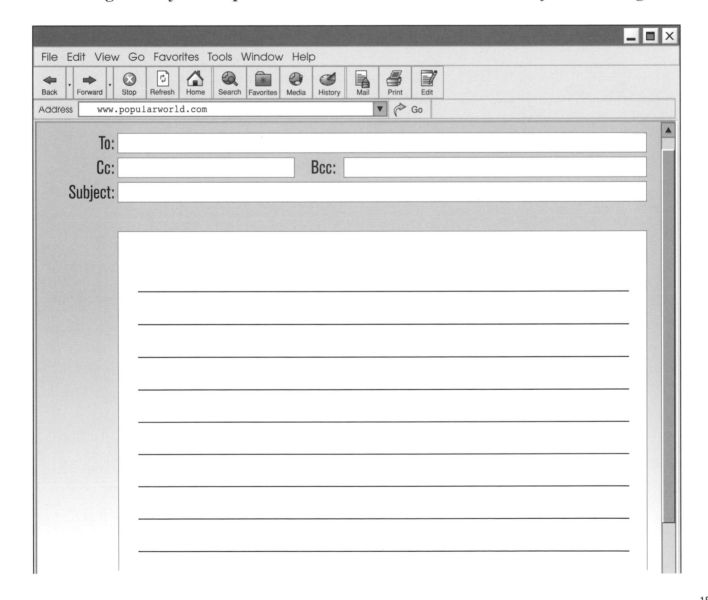

The Formal Letter or E-mail

In contrast with the informal letter or e-mail, this is a more **formal** way of communication, often written with a specific purpose in mind, e.g. to explain, to get things done, to complain, etc. A more formal tone has to be maintained.

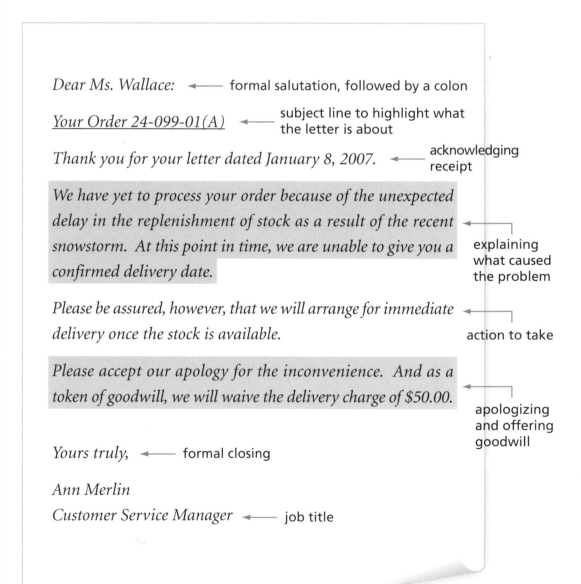

Dear Ms. Wallace: ← formal salutation, followed by a colon

Your Order 24-099-01(A) ← subject line to highlight what the letter is about

Thank you for your letter dated January 8, 2007. ← acknowledging receipt

We have yet to process your order because of the unexpected delay in the replenishment of stock as a result of the recent snowstorm. At this point in time, we are unable to give you a confirmed delivery date. ← explaining what caused the problem

Please be assured, however, that we will arrange for immediate delivery once the stock is available. ← action to take

Please accept our apology for the inconvenience. And as a token of goodwill, we will waive the delivery charge of $50.00. ← apologizing and offering goodwill

Yours truly, ← formal closing

Ann Merlin
Customer Service Manager ← job title

C. **Imagine you are the president of the school computer club. Write an e-mail to the marketing manager of a video game company requesting a group visit to the company for the members of your club.**

Your e-mail should include the following details:

- Purpose of the visit
- Any particular aspects that you are interested in
- Number of members to take part in the visit
- Date and time preferred

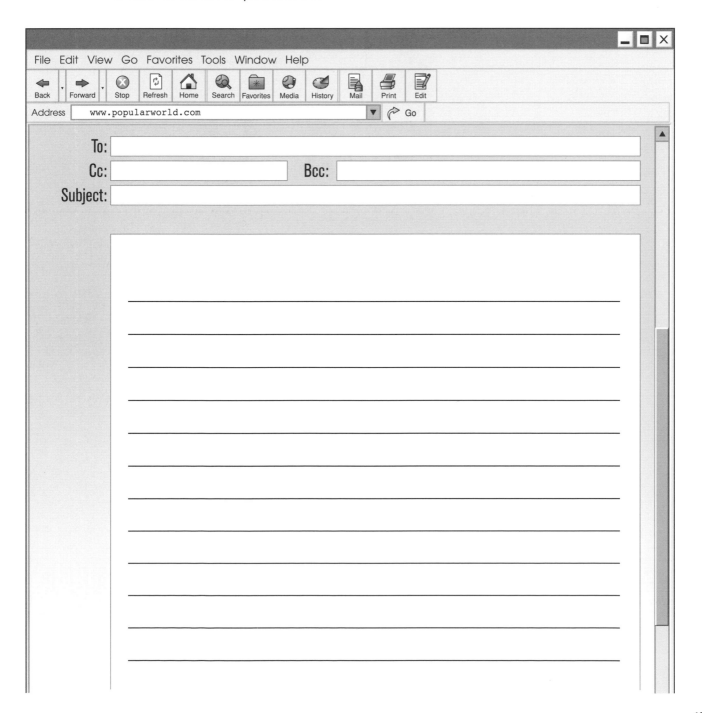

10 Descriptive Writing (1)

In **descriptive writing**, we describe in detail the physical appearance, features, and characteristics of something or someone as well as our thoughts and feelings about that something or someone.

There are two types of descriptive writing.

Objective Description

An **objective description** describes something factually and truthfully. Facts and figures are often used.

Example: *The Eiffel Tower is as tall as a 75-storey building, weighs more than 10 000 tonnes, and is made of iron.*

Subjective Description

A **subjective description** describes the feelings, emotions, and opinions of the writer.

Example: *The Eiffel Tower is my favourite place in Paris. Climbing up to the top of the tower is exhausting but well worthwhile as the view over the city is simply breathtaking.*

A. Read the description of the CN Tower and consider whether the underlined phrases are objective descriptions (O) or subjective descriptions (S).

> *By combining objective and subjective descriptions, we can make our writing both informative and interesting.*

The CN Tower <u>inspires a sense of pride and inspiration for Canadians</u> (1.   ) and <u>a sense of awe for tourists</u> (2.   ). Located in the heart of the Entertainment District of Downtown Toronto, the CN Tower is <u>easily accessible from Union Station</u> (3.   ) as well as many major streets and highways. At a height of 553.33 metres, the CN Tower is <u>the world's tallest free-standing structure</u> (4.   ). Each year, about 2 million people visit the CN Tower to <u>take in the breathtaking view</u> (5.   ) and <u>enjoy all the exciting attractions</u> (6.   ) it has to offer.

B. Read the following short paragraphs and underline the subjective adjectives that reflect the writer's opinion.

Shania Twain is a remarkable Canadian singer and songwriter who has enjoyed immense success in the country and pop music genres. Her third album "Come on Over" is the biggest-selling album of all time by a female artist, and the seventh biggest-selling album in music history, and she is the only female artist to have three albums certified Diamond by the RIAA.

Twain's debut album in 1993 was unsatisfactory as she was forced by her record company to work with Nashville songwriters, and she only got to co-write one of the songs, and felt that the album was not really her own.

Things changed when the legendary rock producer Robert "Mutt" Lange heard Shania's original songs and singing and thought she held promise.

He offered to produce her and to write songs with her. After many telephone conversations, they met in person at Nashville's Fan Fair in June 1993. Soon their professional relationship took a romantic turn, and they were married on December 28, 1993.

Lange and Twain instantly formed a successful partnership, and Twain has often commented that the reason they work so well is they are so different; after all, Lange is 17 years older than Twain.

Describing People

When writing about a person, it is not enough just to describe how the person looks. We also need to write how he or she behaves and thinks. Using descriptive adjectives and phrases adds details to our descriptions.

Example:　*My grandmother is old, has nice hair and fine eyes, and is funny.*

My 74-year-old grandmother has shiny white hair, kind blue eyes, and loves to make people laugh.

C. **Put the following descriptive adjectives and phrases in the appropriate boxes.**

bearded	blonde	booming	chubby
curly	elderly	elegant	fashionable
fresh-faced	generous	greasy	handsome
youngish	muscular	shapely	youthful
skinny	lanky	sweet	teenage
trendy	hard-working	helpful	middle-aged
with rosy cheeks	with thick lips	coarse	intelligent
fluffy	clean-shaven	musical	with pitcher ears

Hair and Facial Features	
Age	
Build	
Personality	
Voice	
Dress	

D. Write a brief description of each of the following people. Describe all the suggested aspects.

1. Tiger Woods
   - Facial features
   - Height and build
   - The personality traits that make him famous

   _____

   _____

   _____

   _____

   _____

   _____

2. My Dad
   - Facial features
   - Height and build
   - Personality and behaviour

   _____

   _____

   _____

   _____

3. Me
   - Age
   - Facial features
   - Height and build
   - Personality

   _____

   _____

   _____

   _____

11 Descriptive Writing (2)

Describing Things and Events

When we write about a thing or an event, try to think how our five senses respond to it. At the same time, compare it to familiar sights, sounds, textures, tastes, or smells.

Examples:

Sense	Description
Sight	The Eiffel Tower stands as tall as a 75-storey building.
Hearing	It made a sound similar to running water.
Touch	The pouch had the feel of soft, polished leather.
Taste	The cake tastes like coffee.
Smell	The aroma reminded me of freshly-picked cherries.

A. Describe each of the following according to the sense indicated by comparing it to something similar.

1. the new pyjamas (sense of touch)

   _____

   _____

2. the beat of the drum (sense of hearing)

   _____

   _____

3. Lake Ontario (sense of sight)

   _____

   _____

4. the Danish (sense of taste)

   _____

   _____

5. the tea (sense of smell)

_____

_____

6. the baseball game (sense of sight and hearing)

_____

_____

7. the birthday cake (sense of smell and taste)

_____

_____

B. Write a short paragraph describing each of the following things or events.

1. a festival

_____

_____

_____

_____

_____

2. a pet or an animal

_____

_____

_____

_____

3. a landmark

_____

_____

_____

_____

Organizing Descriptive Writing

In descriptive writing, we set the scene with an introduction, followed by the body, which contains detailed descriptions about people, things, places, or events. We conclude the writing by summarizing the descriptions.

C. Read the following notes for a descriptive article. Number the items for the introduction 1, those for the body 2, and those for the conclusion 3.

- Brief descriptions of the supporting characters _____

- Explanation of what happens on a particular day _____

- Amusing description of the story's outcome _____

- Description of the main character's daily life _____

- Name and background of the main character _____

- Summary of what the main character learns from the event _____

- Who is in the story _____

- Where the story takes place _____

- Explanation of the main character's behaviour _____

- Description of what the characters do to one another _____

- Description of a memorable event about the main character _____

- An unexpected twist and turn _____

D. Write about a person you admire. Use specific details and a combination of objective and subjective descriptions to make your writing both informative and interesting.

A Writing Guide

- Introduce the person: Who is he/she? What does he/she do?

- Describe the person in detail: appearance, personality, etc.

- Analyze the person: achievements, interesting things about him/her, philosophy of life, etc.

- Recommend the person: Why do you admire him/her? What can you learn from him/her?

_____

_____

_____

_____

_____

_____

_____

_____

_____

_____

_____

_____

_____

12 Factual Writing

Writing about Facts

At school, we are often asked to collect information, organize it, and put all the facts in writing. This calls for the ability to group the related facts and put them in a logical sequence for presentation.

Below are steps to follow for organizing facts before writing:

1. Read all the facts we gathered.
2. Organize the facts by grouping them according to common topics.
3. Put the groups of facts in order of presentation. Decide which should come first, which should be next, and so on.
4. Expand the facts into sentences by using descriptive words.
5. Write an interesting topic sentence for each group of facts.
6. In the concluding paragraph, either summarize your writing or lead the reader to think further about the topic.

A. Read the text below and list ten facts about the Royal Ontario Museum. Your list can be in point form.

The Royal Ontario Museum (ROM) is in Toronto, Ontario. It is Canada's largest museum of human cultures and natural history, as well as the fifth largest museum in North America. Visitors can enjoy the ROM's permanent galleries, changing exhibitions, and public programs. There are more than six million items on display — ranging from dinosaurs to Near Eastern to Canadian history.

The Royal Ontario Museum was officially opened on March 14, 1914 by The Duke of Connaught, then Governor General of Canada. Its original building was designed by Toronto architects Frank Darling and John A. Pearson.

When the museum's site was first chosen, it was still at the edge of Toronto's built-up area, away from the city's business district. The location was chosen for its proximity to the University of Toronto. The original building was constructed on the western edge of the property along the university's Philosopher's Walk. Established in 1912 by the provincial government, the Royal Ontario Museum was operated by the University of Toronto until 1955. Now an independent institution, the ROM still maintains close relations with the university, sharing expertise and resources.

The museum has recently completed a major renovation and expansion project known as Renaissance ROM. Renaissance ROM brings to life new architecture by Daniel Libeskind, alongside the renovated original architecture, creating 300 000 square feet of space.

Facts about the
Royal Ontario Museum

1. _____

2. _____

3. _____

4. _____

5. _____

6. _____

7. _____

8. _____

9. _____

10. _____

B. **Read the facts about Prince Edward Island. Organize the facts and write a short article about the Island. Think of a good title for your writing.**

Facts about Prince Edward Island

- named in honour of Edward, Duke of Kent (father of Queen Victoria) in 1799

- the smallest of the Canadian provinces both in size and population

- capital city: Charlottetown

- located in the Gulf of St. Lawrence on Canada's east coast

- separated from mainland Canada, New Brunswick, and Nova Scotia by the Northumberland Strait

- about 1.2 million visitors annually

- plenty to do on PEI: delicious seafood suppers, uncrowded beaches, more than a dozen golf courses

- made famous by *Anne of Green Gables* published in 1908

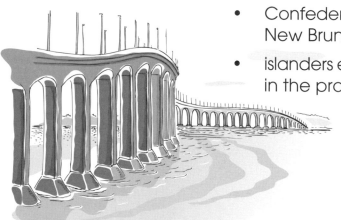

- Confederation Bridge (12.9 km) between PEI and New Brunswick opened in 1997

- islanders eat lots of potatoes since they are grown in the province

- lobsters, mussels, and seafood popular; readily available

Title: _____

Opening Paragraph:

_____

_____

_____

_____

_____

_____

Body Paragraphs:

_____

_____

_____

_____

_____

_____

_____

_____

_____

_____

_____

_____

_____

_____

Concluding Paragraph:

_____

_____

_____

_____

_____

_____

_____

_____

_____

Basic Proofreading and Editing (1)

After writing, we need to spend some time **proofreading** and **editing** our work, paying attention to the following:

- Sentence fragments and run-on sentences
- Use of punctuation
- Subject-Verb Agreement
- Wordiness
- Spelling

Sentence Fragments

Sentence fragments are groups of words that may look like sentences but do not contain complete ideas. They cannot stand on their own.

A. Read the following and put a cross for sentence fragments.

1. Nowhere can the key to the storeroom be found. _____

2. Looking at the issue from another perspective. _____

3. He provided us with a new perspective. _____

4. They might have mistaken it for the original document. _____

5. As long as we could retrieve the original document. _____

6. When all of us were ready for the ceremony. _____

7. Hardly did we recognize Bruno and his sister, Pam. _____

8. Rescuing the crew from the sinking wrecked ship. _____

9. Another meeting will be held to resolve the matter. _____

10. Although they are really eager to resolve the matter. _____

11. After walking for almost an hour in the heat. _____

Run-on Sentences

A **run-on sentence** has at least two sentences put loosely together (e.g. by using a comma) instead of being properly connected by a conjunction or by turning one sentence into a dependent clause.

For some run-on sentences, we can correct them by using proper punctuation marks such as the colon, semicolon, and period.

B. Correct the following run-on sentences. Rewrite them on the lines provided.

1. The weather is fine, we can go hiking this afternoon.

_____

_____

2. It doesn't make sense to me, there is no mention of the procedure.

_____

3. Wait here, don't touch anything.

_____

4. You don't go, I don't go.

_____

5. Many think that he is a capable leader, I don't think so.

_____

6. Let's make a checklist, that way we can be sure that we won't leave anything important behind.

_____

_____

7. The police suspected that he was the mastermind, they interrogated him for hours.

_____

_____

Use of Punctuation

The comma seems to be the most common punctuation mark used. When we go over our writing, check to see if other punctuation marks should be used in place of the comma – the dash, colon, semicolon, period, or parentheses.

C. Read the following paragraphs. Correct the misused punctuation.

1. Toronto; which is the capital of Ontario; is the largest city in Canada. It is home to the world's tallest building, the CN Tower at 553.33 metres and the world's longest street starts at the city's lakeshore (Yonge Street at 1896 kilometres). It also has one of the world's most diverse and multicultural populations. Did you also know that there are more people living in Toronto than in Canada's four Atlantic provinces combined.

2. What game is played on horseback? It's polo, polo is believed to have originated among the Iranian tribes, between 521 and 485 BCE. A polo game is played by two teams each comprising four players, the polo field is 300 yards long, and either 160 yards or 150 yards wide. On each side of the field is a goal, the two goalposts are eight yards apart, the two opposing teams are to score the most goals by hitting the ball through the goal. There are two mounted umpires on the field and a referee standing on the sidelines.

D. Proofread and edit the following text. Look out for sentence fragments, run-on sentences, and the wrong use of punctuation. Rewrite the text in the space provided.

Nova Scotia, Latin for New Scotland. It is located on Canada's southeastern coast. Although Nova Scotia is the second smallest province it is the most populous province in the Maritimes, its capital, Halifax, is the economic and cultural centre of the region.

Some people believe that the Vikings may have settled in Nova Scotia at some time. Though there is little evidence of this. The only authenticated Viking settlement in North America is L'Anse aux Meadows, it establishes the fact that Vikings explored North America 500 years before Christopher Columbus.

There are other stories about early explorations of Nova Scotia. Such as the one about the Italian explorer John Cabot. There is some debate over where he landed, it is believed that he visited present-day Cape Breton in 1497.

14 Basic Proofreading and Editing (2)

In the editing process, we should watch out for subject-verb disagreement.

Example: *Each of the students are asked to complete a questionnaire.* (✘)

<u>Each</u> of the students <u>is</u> asked to complete a questionnaire. (✔)

A. Read each of the following sentences and decide whether or not it is faulty in subject-verb agreement. Rewrite the sentence if it is.

1. There was quite a few people watching when the accident occurred.

   _____

2. He don't seem to understand how serious that can be.

   _____

3. No children were in sight when the teacher arrived.

   _____

4. Everyone are having a great time at the party.

   _____

5. Neither he nor the chairman are aware of the development.

   _____

6. Any one of them are capable of helping you with the project.

   _____

7. Either he or I have to decide whether or not to drop out of the race.

   _____

8. The police was trying to disperse the crowd but without much success.

   _____

9. There is a couple of matters that we need to resolve.

   _____

> ### Wordiness
>
> Writing should be clear and concise. A sentence should contain no unnecessary words.
>
> **Examples:** <u>In my opinion</u>, <u>I think</u> we should go ahead with the plan. (✘)
>
> In my opinion, we should go ahead with the plan. (✔)
>
> or I think we should go ahead with the plan. (✔)
>
> or We should go ahead with the plan. (✔)

B. Rewrite the following sentences in a more concise way by doing away the redundant words or expressions.

1. I couldn't sleep and woke up in the wee hours of the morning at 3:00 a.m.

    _____

2. You should not repeat the same mistake again.

    _____

3. They are in complete agreement with one another.

    _____

4. The troop was surrounded on all sides by the enemy.

    _____

5. In future to come, Jason wants to study medicine and be a doctor.

    _____

6. As I see it, I don't see any reason why a person who is honest should do it that way.

    _____

    _____

7. The reason why he kept telling me about it was because he was worried that I did not believe him.

    _____

    _____

C. **Read the following text on the polar bear. Correct the subject-verb disagreement and do away the wordiness.**

> There are 5 mistakes in subject-verb agreement and 3 cases of wordiness.

The polar bear lives in the Arctic region. It is well-adapted to its habitat with its thick blubber and fur, which insulates it against the bitter cold. The polar bear's fur appear white colour or cream-coloured. This helps camouflage it from its prey. The polar bear hunts well on land and on the sea ice, as well as in the water.

Polar bears use sea ice as a platform to hunt seals, which is the mainstay of their diet. The destruction of their habitat on the Arctic ice, believed to be caused by global warming, are threatening their survival. In actual fact, some scientists warn that polar bears may become extinct within the century.

Most adult male polar bears weigh from 300 to 600 kilograms and measures 2.4 to 2.6 metres in length. According to Guinness World Records 2006, the largest polar bear ever recorded in the book was one shot in Kotzebue Sound, Alaska in 1960 – it weighed 880 kg and was 3.38 m in length! Female polar bears are generally about half the size of males.

D. In the following exercise, focus on spelling. Underline the misspelled words and write the correct ones above them.

The polar bear is the most carniverous member of the bear family, and the one that is most likely to prey on human beings for food. Although it feeds mainly on seals, it eats virtually anything it can kill: birds, rodents, beluga whales, and young walnuses, and very occassionally, other polar bears as well. Polar bears are enormusly strong and powerful. They also haunt very efficently on land due to their speed. In fact, they can easily outrun a humen. They are, however, not as fast as caribou and musk oxen, which is why they subsist almost entirely on seals and young walruses. After all, seals and young walruses are much easier pray.

Polar bears are excellant swimmers and can often be seen in open waters far from land. Resently, polar bears have undertaken longer than usual swims to find prey because of the melting of ice flows. In 2005, there were four recorded drownings as a result of the unusually large ice pack regression.

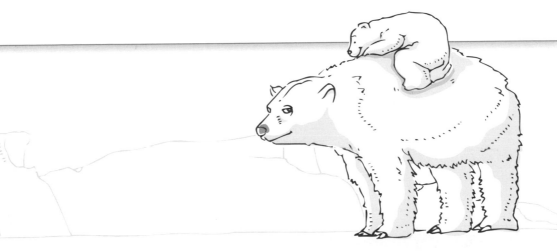

Answers

1 · A Farewell to Pluto

A. 1. (Individual answer)
2. The IAU's new definition of "planet" set new criteria that Pluto does not meet.
3. They reacted with nods of understanding and acceptance, howls of outrage, and shrugs of indifference.
4. (Individual mnemonic)

Your View
(Individual writing)

B. 1. astronomer
2. discovered
3. solar
4. status
5. planet
6. reclassified
7. dwarf
8. orbit
9. neighbourhood

C. 1a. astronomy   b. astronaut   c. astronomer
2a. telescope   b. television   c. telephone
3a. international   b. interschool   c. interchange

D.

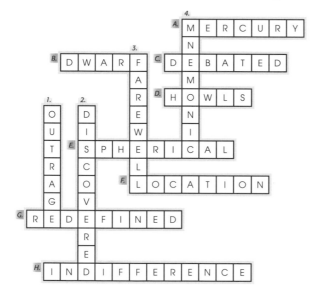

2 · English – a Language that Likes to Lend and Borrow

A. (Individual answers)
B. (Individual answers)
C. 1. Korean   2. Persian
3. Dutch   4. French
5. Chinese   6. Japanese
7. Malay   8. Portuguese
9. Russian   10. Italian
11. Arabic   12. Norwegian
13. German   14. Tamil
15. Spanish
D. (Individual answers)

3 · The Sound of Music

A. Paragraph One: A   Paragraph Two: B
Paragraph Three: C   Paragraph Four: B
B. (Individual writing)
C. (Suggested writing)
1. An Austrian submarine was commanded by Captain Georg von Trapp during World War One.
2. Rodgers and Hammerstein later adapted the story into a popular Broadway musical.
3. A musical group, the Trapp Family Singers, was formed by the family.
4. In 1950, a small ski lodge was opened in Vermont by the von Trapp family.
5. Georg and Maria's son Johannes now manages the Trapp Family Lodge.
6. Maria was convinced by her friend to write about her life.

4 · A History of Avian Flu

A. 1. B   2. C
3. B   4. B
5. B

B. The Middle Ages: The "Black Death" (Bubonic Plague) killed one-third of the population of Europe.
1918: The "Spanish Flu" killed 5% of the world's population.
1957: The "Asian Flu" killed more than 100 000 people.
1968: The "Hong Kong Flu" killed more than 700 000 people.
1997: The virus H5N1 began infecting people in Hong Kong and killed 6 people.
1998: The virus H5N1 killed one person in Hong Kong.
2003: The virus H7N7 infected 83 people and killed one person.
2004: The viruses H5N1 and H7N3 killed people in Vietnam and Thailand, and infected 2 people in Canada.

Your View
(Individual writing)

C. 1. ravaged   2. immunity
3. censorship   4. mortality
5. permafrost   6. mutating
7. strains   8. epidemiologists
9. contagious   10. poultry
11. threat   12. scourges

D. (Suggested definitions)
1. epidemics: widespread occurrences of a disease in a community at a particular time
2. pandemics: prevalent diseases over an entire country or the world
3. plague: contagious bacterial disease characterized by fever and delirium
4. outbreaks: sudden eruptions of disease

5 · The World's Most Unusual Animals

A. 1. The capybara: hippo-like body
2. The jerboa: never drinks
3. The okapi: looks like a cross between a horse and a zebra

4. The tomato frog: inflates into what looks like a big, ripe tomato when threatened
5. The guanaco: its highly prized soft undercoat
6. The long-nosed chimaera: looks like a combination of a serpent and a shark with a pointy duckbill

Your View
(Individual writing)

B. Noun Form

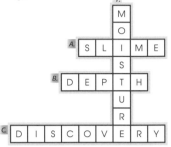

Root Word

Opposite

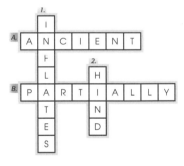

C. (Suggested words)
gooseberry ; rainforests ; overgrown ; undercoat ; streamlined
D. (Individual writing)

---

6 **Extreme Road-tripping: the Pan-American Highway**

A. 1. The "highway" is not a paved, four-lane thoroughfare.
2. The United States had the operation rights.
3. It is a stretch of rainforest and swampland between the Panama Canal and Colombia.
4. The Darién Gap provides a natural barrier to the spread of disease. /
The Darién Gap helps provide stability for the indigenous peoples of the area.

Your View
(Individual writing)

B.

e	x	t	n	i	e	x	t	e	n	s	i	v	e	j	b	k	i	s
p	e	r	m	o	u	e	h	n	f	p	n	x	g	m	c	s	n	j
o	r	a	c	t	e	p	o	s	i	v	t	p	a	o	o	t	t	r
c	t	h	o	r	o	u	g	h	f	a	r	e	p	c	m	a	r	g
k	l	x	n	a	v	m	r	u	d	p	e	r	n	a	m	b	o	u
m	f	n	c	v	c	v	o	v	g	e	p	m	i	l	o	i	p	i
c	o	n	c	e	r	t	e	d	w	a	i	a	o	d	e	l	p	o
l	b	y	e	r	g	t	h	q	e	j	d	n	g	r	c	i	i	s
d	r	h	k	s	c	o	m	m	e	n	c	e	m	e	n	t	d	t
n	e	x	t	e	n	i	s	e	v	k	t	n	s	e	j	y	e	a
i	d	l	e	d	i	b	m	c	o	a	s	t	a	b	l	i	t	y

C. 1. links
2. swampland
3. terrain
4. construction
5. jurisdiction
6. environmental
7. tribal

D. (Individual writing)

---

7 **Weird Teen Trends**

A. 1. Shops everywhere in Thailand were stocking up on fake braces. Some ordinary folk even claimed to be dentists and orthodontists to make money from putting on fake braces for teenaged girls.
2. The government of Thailand declared it an offence to manufacture or sell fake braces.
3. The government of China banned the sale of voodoo dolls and school staff was given authority to confiscate them.

Your View
(Individual writing)

B.

C. (Individual writing)

8 Amelia Earhart

A. Paragraph One: A   Paragraph Two: A
    Paragraph Three: A   Paragraph Four: A
    Paragraph Five: B

B. 1927: became the first woman to fly the Atlantic
    1931: set a world altitude record of 18 415 feet (5613 metres)
    1932: became the first woman to solo the Atlantic
    1935: became the first person to solo from Hawaii to the
          U.S. mainland

C. 1. (Suggested answer)
        She probably saw skill and a lot of determination in
        Amelia.
    2. She was the first woman to fly across the Atlantic. "Lady
        Lindy" was a reference to Charles Lindbergh, who was
        the first person to solo across the Atlantic.
    3. He guided her publicity appearances and
        endorsements, which provided the money necessary for
        a flying career.
    4. (Individual answer)
    5. (Individual answer)

D.

9 The Ultimate Tourist

A. 1. (Suggested answer)
        It is someone with no direct experience of travelling – for
        example, someone who watches travel shows on TV
        instead of venturing out on vacation.
    2. There is nowhere left on Earth to explore. Places that
        once seemed unreachable are now accessible within
        24 hours.
    3. Entrepreneurs around the world have put themselves in
        a race to offer commercial space flights.
    4. An American multi-millionaire named Dennis Tito flew on
        the Russian government's Soyuz spacecraft to the
        International Space Station for a seven-day stay. He had
        paid the Russian government a fee to do this.

Your View
(Individual writing)

B. 1. J   2. I
    3. D   4. F
    5. H   6. A
    7. E   8. G
    9. B   10. C

C. 1. access
    2. future
    3. orbit
    4. tour
    5. establish
    6. destiny
    7. billion
    8. nation

D. (Individual writing)

10 Tooth-in-eye

A. 1. B   2. B
    3. B   4. A
    5. C   6. A

B. 1. procedural
    2. organic
    3. preventive
    4. conceptual
    5. sensory
    6. curable

C. 1. restoration
    2. growth
    3. involvement
    4. occurrence
    5. belief
    6. refraction
    7. performance
    8. removal
    9. entrance
   10. clarity

D. breakthroughs ; commonplace ; eyesight ; eyeball ; thereby
E. 1. put into another place
    2. add to
F. (Individual writing)

11 He Climbed Mount Everest

A. 1. It is someone with two artificial legs.
    2. (Individual answer)
    3. One of his prosthetic legs snapped on his ascent of
        Everest, and he suffered from laryngitis and frostbite of
        the fingers. He also came across a stricken climber high
        on the mountain.
    4. It suggests a "make or break" situation: you either reach
        the summit of Mt. Everest, or you don't because of
        weather conditions. At worst, you may even lose your
        life.

B. (Individual writing)

C.

B.

D. (Suggested writing)
1. I started climbing at a young age. By the age of 20, I was already a professional climber, and worked as a search-and-rescue mountaineer in Aoraki/Mt. Cook National Park. I was the first to climb Mt. Everest with two artificial legs.
2. I would've given up my ascent to help the stricken climber down the mountain.

E. (Individual writing)

12 Ikebana

A. 1. This spiritual endeavour brings calm to our stressful lives. Also, potted flowers can act as nature's air purifiers.
2. It came about when Buddhism was brought to Japan from China and began influencing Japanese arts and culture.
3. a. classic Ikenobo: uses a strict set of rules and geometric sense of space
b. Ohara: uses the shorter-stemmed flowers imported from the West
c. Sogetsu: more free-styling in terms of colour, materials, and space
4. It attempts to recreate the beauty of the outdoors and bring it indoors. For example, a vase fashioned from a bamboo frond is a grove. Also, Ikebana engages you in every step of the art, from growing to choosing your flowers.
5. The act of making a flower arrangement allows you to focus on the activity and express yourself with the flowers' beauty, bringing you great peace of mind.

C. 1. Flower arranging – or Ikebana in Japanese – helps turn one's home into a haven.
2. The act of arranging flowers (and of focusing on an activity) offers us a sense of calm.
3. Ikebana attempts to recreate the beauty of outdoor landscapes – rivers, lakes, gardens, and valleys – and bring it indoors.
4. Ikebana is an ancient art that was first developed – probably as early as the sixth century – by Buddhist priests in Japan.

13 So You Want to Be an Author

A. 1. The writer thinks a book agent does not help much. He or she will ask you for money but may only mail photocopies of your manuscript to publishers, which you can do yourself anyway.
2. It is a way of publishing whereby the author pays a fee to the POD company, and covers the costs of design. The book is produced only when ordered, but will be a bit more expensive than a book published in the traditional fashion.
3. The writer thinks that having a Website, making promotional appearances, and establishing relationships with different organizations are important.
4. (Individual answer)

Your View
(Individual writing)

B.

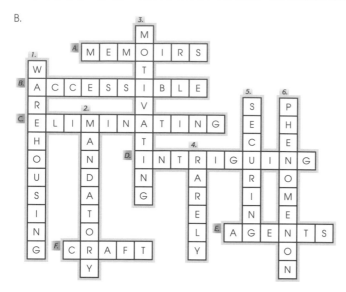

2. • The excavations at Akrotiri are at the island's southern end.
   • The excavations at Akrotiri are of interest to believers in Atlantis.
   • Akrotiri is of interest to those who come for rest and relaxation.

C.

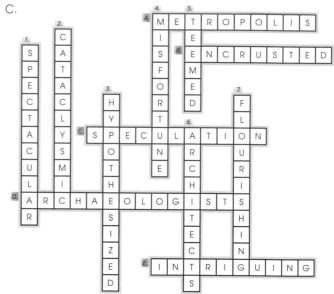

C. Baseball is a popular sport in North America. It was developed in the United States from an early bat-and-ball game called rounders, and it has become the national sport of the United States. In a game of baseball, the pitcher throws a hard, fist-sized ball past the hitting area of a batter and the batter tries to hit it with a bat made of wood or metal. A team scores only when batting, by advancing counter-clockwise past a series of four bases arranged at the corners of a diamond. Each base is 90 feet from the previous one. Professional baseball started in the United States in the 1860s when the first fully professional baseball club, the Cincinnati Red Stockings, was formed and went undefeated against a schedule of semi-professional and amateur teams, as there were no other fully professional baseball teams that year. The first "major league" was the National Association which lasted from 1871 to 1875. The National League was then founded in 1876. Several other major leagues formed and failed, but the American League, established in 1901 as a major league and originating from the minor Western League (1893), was proved to be a success. The two leagues began playing a World Series in 1903.

15 What Is Globalization?

A. (Individual writing)

B.

C. (Suggested writing)
1. Many people oppose globalization but many people embrace it.
2. When a Wal-Mart store opens in China, this is globalization in action.
3. Some say that globalization benefits only rich people since they control most of the wealth in the world.
4. Globalization will continue and its problems will intensify.
5. Globalization benefits the poor too, since job opportunities are now open to the poor, whereas they did not exist in the past.

14 Atlantis

A. 1. Plato wrote about this great civilization, but we do not know exactly what ended it.
   2. They are both believed to be destroyed by a natural disaster, maybe even the same one.
   3. Its magnitude enables us to better imagine what might have wiped out the ancient people of Atlantis.
   4. (Individual writing)
   Your View
   (Individual writing)
B. 1. • It was thought that a natural disaster destroyed the Greek island of Rhodes and its legendary Colossus.
   • The legendary Colossus was the huge statue that stood at the harbour.
   • The huge statue is considered to be one of the seven ancient wonders of the world.

16 The Facts behind the Figures

A. (Individual writing)
B. (Suggested writing)
1. there really was a man named Count Dracula, he was not a vampire.
2. there consider Dracula a national hero because he helped fight off invading armies.
3. the heads of the soldiers he killed on sticks was something Dracula liked to do.
4. destroy property are often referred to as "vandals".
5. was captured by the Vandals in the year 455.
6. the depiction of her on ancient coins, Cleopatra had a big neck and sharp features.
7. was the Egyptian queen ; united the Egyptian and Roman empires.
C. (Individual writing)

17 Point Pelee National Park of Canada

A. 1. It is the most southerly point on mainland Canada and extends as far south as northern California.
2. It is filled with Monarch butterflies in their migration flyway.
3. It offers an unrivalled collection of plants and animals in a wide range of habitats.
4. They were people who settled on unoccupied land without any legal rights.
5. A group of duck hunters / enthusiasts saw the value of preserving Point Pelee and convinced the federal government to protect it, which it did, making it a national park in 1918.
6. (Individual answer)
B.

S K I R M I S H E S
Q
L U S H
P A
O T
R T M
T E I
A B O R I G I N A L
G S R U N R I V A L L E D
P O C K E T A
E T
N F O R E S I G H T
S O
U U N I Q U E
O A S I S

C. (Individual writing)

18 The Art of Cubism

A. Braque and Picasso's Works:
- subject is "deconstructed" and then "re-assembled" in an abstract way
- use assortment of shapes and angles
- has very little sense of depth
- monochromatic and dull in colour
Impressionists' Works:
- subjects are often landscapes and people in outdoor settings
- emphasize the effect of light
- bright and vivid in colour
B. 1. It came about in 1908 when a French art critic described a painting by Braque as being "full of little cubes".
2. He was experimenting with his paintings, adding objects like chair caning, wood, and newspaper, using glue and paint.
3. It is disjointed and irregular. For example, composer Igor Stravinsky wrote a Cubist piece that incorporated jazz with darker Russian music.

Your View
(Individual writing)
C. 1. evolve
2. cube
3. character
4. impress
5. construct
6. differ
D. (Individual writing)
E. (Individual writing)

1 Subject-Verb Agreement

A. 1. Everyone involved in the play was happy to learn that all the tickets were sold out.
3. Some of the judges do not like the criteria given to them.
4. Each of the team members is reminded to attend the practice session.
5. Everybody knows that it is wrong to take advantage of someone who actually needs your help.
7. Someone among the children has left the book here.

B. 1. likes   2. has   3. Has
4. needs   5. are

C. 1. was   2. live   3. say
4. is   5. do not want

D. 1. am   2. was   3. wants
4. are   5. stands

E. Jim Carrey is one of those who never ~~gives~~ **give** up their hopes and ambitions. In fact, when he was just ten years old, Carrey mailed his résumé to The Carol Burnett Show in the hope of joining them as a comedian! Noticing his talent, Carrey's high school teachers gave him a few minutes at the end of each school day to do a stand-up comedy for his classmates. It was certainly a great way to wrap up the day as everyone ~~were~~ **was** entertained.

When Carrey was 13 years old, his father lost his job. He, as well as his father, ~~were~~ **was** forced to move out of their house and live in their van instead. To help out, Carrey began working eight-hour shifts each day after school. The long hours exhausted Carrey and left him with little time to focus on homework and studies. This took a toll on Carrey's grades. To motivate himself, he once wrote a cheque for $20 million and vowed that he would cash it in some day. Both Jim himself and his father ~~was~~ **were** confident that Carrey could make it. Sadly though, his father passed away a few years later. Carrey then put the cheque inside the pocket of his father's funeral clothes. Years later, Jim finally made it big in Hollywood as a comedian. Most of the Canadians, be they Jim's fans or not, ~~admires~~ **admire** his fighting spirit and his strong desire to succeed.

F. (Individual writing)

2 Quantifiers and Determiners

A. For Countable Nouns:
many ; a few ; several ; a couple of ; none of
For Uncountable Nouns:
not much ; a bit of ; a great deal of ; a little
For both Countable Nouns and Uncountable Nouns:
some ; a lot of ; a lack of ; enough ; all of ; plenty of

B. 1. many ; few / several ; plenty of / a lot of
2. a bit of / a little ; plenty of / a lot of ; some
3. a bit of ; None of ; enough

C. 1. few   2. a few   3. little   4. Few
5. a little   6. a few

D. 1. The / That ; a ; an ; his
2. The / This ; His ; the ; an ; our / the ; a / the ; this ; it
3. an ; the ; the ; those

E. Basketball has developed into one of the most popular sports in the world, but did you know that almost three thousand years ago, people were already playing a game similar to basketball?

It all happened in Mexico, in an area called the Yucatan Peninsula in the 7th century BCE. The game, called "pok-a-tok", was played in a court made with stone walls. There was a goal at each end made from a flat stone with a hole in the middle. Like NBA games, "pok-a-tok" attracted many spectators.

In the game, the players had to get a rubber ball stuffed with "sacred" plants into the goal. There were many unusual rules. Unlike basketball players today, the "pok-a-tok" players could not handle the ball with their hands. They were allowed to move the ball using only their hips, thighs, and knees! Try doing that with a ball and you'll know how skilful those players must have been. However skilful they might have been, though, they could never do the acrobatic slam dunk!

3 Modifiers

A. 2. The players tried really hard to turn the game around.
3. Steve isn't feeling too well; he has a mild fever.
4. In order not to be discovered, he walked into the room slowly and quietly.
5. They are working hard to make sure that they can meet the deadline.
6. He did it so badly that he dared not submit it to the committee.
8. The plan should have been more carefully executed.
9. The refugees are in desperate need of food, clothing, and medicine.

B. 1. A   2. C   3. C

C. 1. good ; well ; badly
2. bad ; well ; good ; badly

D. 1. A   2. A   3. B   4. A
5. A   6. A   7. B

E. (Suggested writing)
1. To train a dog to be obedient, you need patience.
2. When you take a grammar quiz, concentration is everything.
3. To be ready for the game, you need more practice.
4. After my car was washed, it sparkled like new.
5. After talking with the veterinarian, we found out that our dog needed surgery.
6. Having worked for the company for more than three decades, Mr. Sutherland was fired by the manager.
7. Before leaving for work, I played with my cat for a while.
8. To conserve energy, we will turn off the air-conditioning system after six.

4 Prefixes and Suffixes

A. (Suggested answers)
1. geology ; geography   2. audible ; auditorium
3. manuscript ; manufacture   4. thermometer ; odometer
5. television ; telephone   6. sympathy ; pathetic
7. astronomy ; astronaut   8. benefit ; benevolent
9. operator ; operation   10. juror ; jurisdiction
11. physique ; physics   12. transfer ; refer

B.
1. half
2. do the opposite
3. one
4. again
5. two
6. above, over
7. thousand
8. around
9. hundred
10. many
11. not
12. across
13. three
14. between, among
15. wrongly
16. together
17. opposite to
18. before

C. (Suggested answers)
1. careful ; careless ; carelessness ; carefully ; carelessly ; caring
2. likely ; likelihood ; likeness ; liking ; likable
3. sharpen ; sharply ; sharpness ; sharper ; sharpest
4. depending ; dependant ; dependable ; dependence ; dependency
5. watchful ; watching ; watchable ; watchfully
6. fearless ; fearful ; fearlessly ; fearfully
7. national ; nationalized ; nationalization ; nationally
8. pretending ; pretentious ; pretender
9. friendly ; friendship ; friendliness

D. (Individual writing)

5 Tricky Words

A. 1a. imminent
b. eminent
2a. lose
b. loose
3a. adopt
b. adapt
4a. respectable
b. respectful
5a. effect
b. affect

B. (Suggested answers)
1. The principal believed that neither Tim nor Eva should be held responsible.
2. He was well-known for his anti-social behaviour.
3. They were so excited when the star player came and signed on their caps.
4. Besides Timmy, I think that Rob, Cecil, and Sam were all involved.
5. The man threatened him with a knife and robbed him of his wallet.
6. She should be sensible enough not to repeat the same mistake.
7. His childlike curiosity enables him to stay creative and adventurous.

C. (Individual writing)

D. 1a. into
b. in
2a. its
b. it's
3a. fewer
b. less
4a. each other
b. one another
5a. wander
b. wonder
6a. then
b. than

E. If you look at a medieval map of the world, you might **wonder** (wander) why there are **fewer** (less) continents **than** (then) a modern map and why there is a large section labelled as "the unknown".

The truth is, in the old days people usually sought **advice** (advise) from those **respectable** (respectful) priests, who, in turn, would refer to the Bible for answers. Since the Bible often mentioned the four corners of the Earth, it was assumed **then** (than) that the world was square and flat.

People were actually afraid to sail too far out **into** (in) the ocean for fear that they might sail right off the edge of the world! It was quite some time before people **accepted** (excepted) that the world was not flat.

6 Some Less Common Tenses

A. 1. ✔ 2. 3. 4.
5. ✔ 6. 7. 8.
9. ✔ 10. ✔
B. 1. 2. 3. ✔ 4. ✔
5. ✔

C. 1. reached ; had departed
2. had met
3. decided ; had reminded
4. had finished ; went
5. came ; had already left

D. (Individual writing)

E. The Boeing 747 is often referred to as the Jumbo Jet. With its upper-deck hump, the Jumbo Jet **is** (had been) the most recognizable icon of air travel. It is the largest passenger plane, as it is ~~used to be~~ able to accommodate a maximum of 524 passengers. Soon, however, it will ~~have~~ become the second largest, when the Airbus A380 is officially put into service.

Unlike the hump on the Jumbo Jet, the A380's upper deck extends along the entire length of the fuselage. This allows for a spacious cabin with 50% more floor space than the Boeing 747. In fact, an A380 jet plane can be configured to carry more than 850 passengers! No wonder people are **have** (used to) calling it the Superjumbo. Commercial flights **have** (had) been scheduled to begin in 2007 after lengthy delays due to technical glitches.

Both the 747 and the A380 can fly at high-subsonic speeds of 900 kilometres per hour, but in terms of intercontinental range, the A380 can fly non-stop for 15 000 km while the 747's maximum range is 13 000 km.

So, after the A380, what will **be** (have been) the next big thing that flies in the air?

7 Use of Capital Letters

A. 1. The Lunar New Year is celebrated not only by the Chinese but also by the Japanese.
3. No one seemed to have any idea of the origin of April Fool's Day.
4. When we finally reached the hotel, we were told that all the rooms had been booked.
5. The 2010 Winter Olympics will be held in Vancouver, British Columbia.
6. Mr. Jones was the chairman of the committee between 2003 and 2005.

B. 1. Last weekend, Uncle Bob took us to an ice-fishing trip up north.

2. In fall, the migratory birds fly south to Mexico to stay away from the bitter cold in winter.
3. The principal showed the new teacher, Mrs. Williamson, the way to the library.
4. Mom is excited about having a chance to meet up with Aunt Sue and Uncle Joe but Dad doesn't seem to be too enthusiastic about it.
5. Bahrain is a borderless island country in the Persian Gulf in the Middle East.
6. This year's Parents' Night will be held on September 19 and Jonathan is on the organizing committee.
7. They enjoy Math lessons because they find their Math teacher both knowledgeable and entertaining.
8. He is planning to move to a little town called Lakeview, which is about an hour's drive from Belville.
9. She introduced me to her father (he looked much younger than I'd thought) and we had a good chat.
10. Mrs. Patterson headed south down the road and then turned into Wellington Avenue.

C.
1. 101 Ways to Decorate Your Living Room
2. What Your Doctor Doesn't Want You to Know
3. The Old Man and the Sea
4. The Revenge of the Robots
5. All You Want to Know about the Web
6. Dead or Alive
7. The Bottom of the Ninth
8. The Bermuda Triangle – Fact or Fiction
9. Somewhere Out There
10. What Dogs Like and Dislike

D. The Winter Olympics is finally returning to <u>north</u> [North] America eight years after Salt <u>lake city</u> [Lake City] hosted the games in 2002. In 2010, Vancouver will be hosting the games, which will be the <u>Third</u> [third] Olympics hosted by Canada (<u>Previously,</u> [previously] Canada was home to the 1976 <u>summer</u> [Summer] Olympics in Montreal and the 1988 Winter Olympics in Calgary). And for the first time ever, the opening and closing <u>Ceremonies</u> [ceremonies] for a Winter Olympics will be held indoors.

Before bidding for hosting the games, Vancouver's residents were asked in a <u>Referendum</u> [referendum] whether they accepted the responsibilities of the <u>Host City</u> [host city] should it win its bid. Sixty-four <u>Percent</u> [percent] of the residents accepted the challenge. It was the first time such a <u>Referendum</u> [referendum] had been successful.

Vancouver finally won the bidding process to host the Olympics on July 2, 2003.

The Canadian Olympic Committee has pledged to win the most <u>Gold Medals</u> [gold medals] at the 2010 Winter Olympics. To achieve this lofty goal, *Own <u>The</u> [the] Podium 2010* has been launched. It is a collaborative effort supported by all of Canada's winter national sport federations. The focus is to provide additional resources and high-performance programming for Canadian athletes and coaches to help Canadian athletes achieve podium success in 2010.

---

8 Some More Members of the Punctuation Family

A.
1. Remember what John F. Kennedy said: "We need men who can dream of things that never were."
2. The coach needed two things from us: our desire to win and our faith in him.
3. Few realized that the plan had one major flaw: it involved too much investment at the outset.
4. They knew what to do next: report the case to the principal.
5. Do you know who said this: "Truth is what stands the test of experience"?
6. If we analyze a paragraph, we often notice these three components: the topic sentence, the supporting details, and the concluding sentence.
7. There remained one problem: we had to win Jeffrey over.
8. The zoo expects some more animals to arrive in the next couple of days: two cheetahs, one gorilla, one kangaroo, and six penguins.

B.
1. The batter keyed up; he waited patiently for the pitch.
2. The couple invited several distinguished guests to the reception: Mrs. Weir, Principal of St. Peter's School; Professor Swire, the University of Toronto; Mr. Sam Watson, MPP Scarborough East, and David Nunn, Executive Director, The Knowledge Bank, Ontario Chapter.
3. There was only one thing remaining on her to-do list: make an appointment with Mr. Cook on or before Tuesday.2
4. He didn't sleep well; it was too hot and humid.
5. As soon as she realized the problem, she asked for her father's help; it was too late though.
6. The doctor can tell that there is something wrong with her: she is panting.
7. No one knew what was going on; the situation simply ran out of control.
8. You need the following to succeed: motivation, commitment, and perseverance.
9. Grandmother used to get up very early; she enjoyed the atmosphere of daybreak.
10. We stuffed our backpacks with everything: snacks, utensils, tools, and even shoes!

C. Albert Einstein (March 14, 1879 – April 18, 1955) is considered one of the greatest physicists of all time. He is best known as the creator of the theory of relativity (specifically $E=mc^2$). In fact, the name "Einstein" has become synonymous with great intelligence and genius.

At his birth, Albert's mother was worried about her infant: his head was so large and oddly shaped! Einstein also spoke much later than the average child. He recalled that he did not begin speaking until the age of three and only did so hesitantly even beyond the age of nine. Because of Einstein's late speech development and his later childhood tendency to ignore any subject in school that bored him (focusing instead only on what interested him), some observers at the time suggested that he might be retarded.

When Einstein was young (probably at the age of five), his father showed him a small pocket compass, and Einstein believed that the needle must have been affected by something in empty space. He later described the experience as one of the most revelatory events of his life.

D.
1. I don't know what you mean by "categorically".
2. L.M. Montgomery's "Anne of Green Gables" was first published in 1908.
3. Perhaps you should clarify with Mrs. Sutherland the term

"stimulated emission".

4. The reporter asked, "Where were you when the accident happened?"
5. "What is the expected increase rate?" asked the manager.
6. They said Dr. Seuss used only 50 words to write "Green Eggs and Ham".
7. In this context, "pristine" means remaining in a pure state.
8. "How can you say that you have nothing to do with it?" complained Fred.
9. When told not to make any more such mistakes, Jason rebuked, "Freedom is not worth having if it does not include the freedom to make mistakes."
10. She wrote a feature article entitled "The Poverty Problem – a Time Bomb".
11. "There is no way I can tell that this is a better alternative," explained Barry.
12. "Pride and Prejudice" was written by Jane Austen, who also wrote "Sense and Sensibility".

Review 1

A. 1. is   2. Is   3. know   4. Has
   5. think   6. prefer   7. want   8. has
   9. plays   10. is
B. (Individual writing)
C. 1. A   2. B   3. A   4. A
D. 1. hardly   2. really   3. hard
   4. bad   5. badly   6. real
   7. good ; well   8. quickly ; quick
E. 3. Whistling down the garden path, Bill suddenly had a brilliant idea.
   5. With plenty of time to spare, Jeff built another new cabinet!
   8. Cartwheeling across the field, Catherine can hardly contain her/the excitement.
   10. Daydreaming again, Rose was asked by Mrs. Cook why she was staring at the sky.
F. 1. the   2. a   3. the   4. her
   5. this   6. a   7. a   8. a
   9. their   10. that   11. two   12. this
   13. her   14. the   15. that   16. the
   17. some   18. their
G. 1.   2. ✔   3. ✔
   4.   5. ✔   6.
H. 1. three: trilingual ; triplets ; trillium ; tricycle
   above: superscript ; superintendent ; superhero ; supernatural
   far off: telepathy ; television ; telephone ; telegram
   2. (Individual writing)
I. 1. will have finished / is going to have finished
   2. will have mastered / is going to have mastered
   3. finishes
   4. had been
   5. had heard
   6. will have come / is going to have come
   7. had volunteered
   8. had leapt
J. The collection of German and French fairy tales known as *Grimm's Fairy Tales* (called *Children's and Household Tales* in English) was published throughout the 1800s by Jacob and Wilhelm Grimm, two German brothers with an interest in ancient fairy tales. Many stories from their collection have enjoyed widespread appeal, such as "Hansel and Gretel"; "Sleeping Beauty"; "Rapunzel"; "Rumpelstiltskin"; "The Golden Goose", and "The Singing Bone". Because the brothers' father died when they were young, leaving the mother to take care of the family in harsh circumstances,

some psychologists have argued that this influenced the way the Brothers Grimm presented the mother figure in their stories, like the stepmother in "Sleeping Beauty" and the wicked witch in "Hansel and Gretel". Although the collection has been criticized for not being suitable for children (as in the violence involved in punishing some of the villains), *Grimm's Fairy Tales* has a huge influence in literary culture: it ranks behind only the Bible and the works of Shakespeare in sales, and has been translated into many different languages around the world.

9   Some Basic Spelling Rules

A – C. (Individual answers)
D. ~~decieful~~ ; deceitful   ~~worryed~~ ; worried
   ~~plyed~~ ; plied   ~~inclinning~~ ; inclining
   ~~plagueing~~ ; plaguing
E.

F.   (Individual writing)

10   Phrases

A. 1. of   2. gemstone   3. after
   4. leaving   5. box   6. well
   7. fence   8. hard-working   9. with
   10. wearing   11. Under   12. accident
B. 1. NP   2. PP   3. PP   4. AVP
   5. VP   6. NP   7. AP
C. (Individual writing)
D. 1. ADJ   2. ADL   3. ADL   4. ADL
   5. ADJ   6. ADL   7. ADJ
E – F. (Individual writing)

11   Adverbs, Adverb Phrases, and Adverb Clauses

A – B. (Individual writing)
C. 1. Wherever he goes
   2. Before the coach arrived
   3. because Matt and Sue misbehaved in class
   4. so that he had some time to rehearse
   5. Although we seldom see each other now
   6. If you listened to me
D. Have you been to an ice hotel before? In January each year, there is one built near Montmorency Falls, Quebec <u>when the temperature is low enough</u>. Come April and the hotel will melt.

The walls of the ice hotel are more than a metre thick <u>so that it is structurally safe</u>. <u>Although the beds in the ice hotel are all made of ice blocks</u>, you won't feel cold <u>because they are lined with deer furs and covered with mattresses and arctic sleeping bags.</u> All other furniture is made of ice, too. In addition to using ice glasses, the bar also serves cold cuts on ice plates. The bathrooms are heated, but they are in a separate insulated structure.

It is quite an experience spending a night in a hotel made of ice – to enjoy the beauty of winter. The ice hotel is absolutely spectacular, <u>especially when it is all lit up at night</u>. There is one thing that is somewhat annoying, though: <u>if you feel the urge to go to the bathroom in the middle of the night</u>, you'll have to get dressed to bear the cold along the corridor leading to the heated bathrooms.

12 Superfluous Words and Phrases

A. (Suggested answers)
1. now	2. whether	3. because
4. each / every	5. without	6. to
7. and	8. because	9. many
10. if	11. because	12. except

B. (Cross out these words.)
1. terms of	2. In my opinion
3. is the kind of man who	4. as a matter of fact
5. again	6. on all sides
7. personal	8. back
9. together	10. very
11. other ; choice	12. together
13. in shape	14. absolutely

C. (Suggested writing)
1. There will be a celebration before the game.
2. They sailed along the river in a houseboat.
3. We understand that the show will be postponed.
4. There was little precipitation in May.
5. Although we made a profit, he did not consider this deal a worthwhile one.

D. Thousands of years ago, people already knew how to make hot air balloons that could rise <u>up</u> into the air. In China, unmanned hot air balloons <u>without passengers</u>, called Kongming lanterns, were reportedly used for military signalling in the Three Kingdoms era.

Some people also believe that hot air balloons were <u>believed to be</u> used by the Nazca Indians of Peru some 1500 years ago as a tool for designing vast drawings on the Nazca plain.

The first hot air balloon capable of carrying passengers were built by the brothers Josef and Etienne Montgolfier in France. They were from a family of paper manufacturers. <u>The reason why</u> they managed to invent the hot air balloon <u>was</u> because they had noticed the ash rising in fires. <u>Due to the fact that</u> they had been successful with unmanned balloons, they started to experiment with flights that carried animals. The first balloon flight with human beings on board took place on <u>the date of</u> October 19, 1783. The first hot air balloons were basically cloth bags with a smoky fire on a grill attached to the bottom. They could catch fire easily and be destroyed upon landing <u>on the ground</u>.

Hot air balloons are able to fly <u>above the ground</u> to extremely high altitudes <u>in the sky</u>. The highest hot air balloon flight reached <u>an altitude of</u> 21 290 metres. The furthest that a hot air balloon managed to fly was <u>a distance of</u> 7671.91 kilometres. The longest duration that a hot air balloon flight ever made was 50 hours and 38 minutes.

Today, hot air balloons are used primarily for recreation. <u>As</u>

<u>a matter of fact</u>, there are some 7000 hot air balloons operating in the United States.

(Rewritten passage)
Thousands of years ago, people already knew how to make hot air balloons that could rise into the air. In China, unmanned hot air balloons, called Kongming lanterns, were reportedly used for military signalling in the Three Kingdoms era.

Some people also believe that hot air balloons were used by the Nazca Indians of Peru some 1500 years ago as a tool for designing vast drawings on the Nazca plain.

The first hot air balloon capable of carrying passengers were built by the brothers Josef and Etienne Montgolfier in France. They were from a family of paper manufacturers. They managed to invent the hot air balloon because they had noticed the ash rising in fires. Since they had been successful with unmanned balloons, they started to experiment with flights that carried animals. The first balloon flight with human beings on board took place on October 19, 1783. The first hot air balloons were basically cloth bags with a smoky fire on a grill attached to the bottom. They could catch fire easily and be destroyed upon landing.

Hot air balloons are able to fly to extremely high altitudes. The highest hot air balloon flight reached 21 290 metres. The furthest that a hot air balloon managed to fly was 7671.91 kilometres. The longest duration that a hot air balloon flight ever made was 50 hours and 38 minutes.

Today, hot air balloons are used primarily for recreation. In fact, there are some 7000 hot air balloons operating in the United States.

13 Clauses

A.
1. I didn't lose my temper ; I was really mad at her
2. The game was tough ; we managed to score in the third quarter
3. They made me captain ; I was the tallest among them
4. you invite her in person ; she won't be coming
5. I opened the closet door ; a mouse darted out
6. The weather turned bad ; we ended up playing chess at John's home

B. (Suggested answers)
Coordinate Clause
he was offered numerous scholarships to major universities
Subordinate Clause
where he set records in track and field
Main Clause
Jackie Robinson attended Pasadena Junior College

C – D. (Individual writing)

14 More on Clauses

A.
1. that was way too long for him
2. where Uncle Jeff used to work
3. who turned 50 last week
4. that Paul was wearing
5. which was released yesterday
6. whom everybody likes

B. (Suggested writing)
1. He was wearing a T-shirt that didn't fit him.
2. This is the place which Mabel was telling us about.
3. The team that was determined to come back big had lost five games in a row.
4. My father, who has never been to any countries in South America, will visit Brazil next week.

5. The library, where Pam's mother works, has a wide collection of storybooks.
6. Mr. Foster has just finished writing a book that is about developing a winning attitude.

C. (Individual writing)

D. 1. ADV   2. ADV   3. N   4. N
   5. N   6. ADV   7. N   8. N
   9. ADV

E. (Individual writing)

15 More on Relative Clauses

A. 1. whom   2. why   3. who
   4. whose   5. that / which   6. that / which
   7. who   8. where   9. when
   10. that / which

B. (Cross out these words.)
   1. that   3. that   6. which   7. that

C. 1. The boy I talked to just now is called Simon.
   2. Alice is wearing the dress her mother made for her.
   3. I like the nifty MP3 player my brother gave me.
   4. The members don't support the plan Ron proposed.

D. 1a. N   b. D   2a. D   b. N
   3a. D   b. N   4a. D   b. N
   5a. D   b. N

E – F. (Individual writing)

16 Types of Sentences

A. 1. S   2. CP   3. CX   4. S
   5. CX   6. S   7. CPX   8. CP
   9. CPX   10. CP

B. If we have to describe pizza to someone who has never seen or eaten it before, how can we go about doing it? Here is Sandy's attempt: "Pizza is an oven-baked, flat, round bread and it is covered with tomato sauce and toppings. There is a wide variety of toppings to choose from for your pizza. Pepperoni, bell peppers, ham, and mushrooms are the most common toppings. The crust of a pizza is plain, but some people prefer to season it with butter, garlic, herbs, or cheese. In Canada, we have our own "Canadian pizza" and this kind of pizza has the topping combination of back bacon, pepperoni, and mushrooms. In Quebec, however, the same topping combination is called a "Québécois Pizza".

(Suggested writing)
Pizza is an oven-baked, flat, round bread that is covered with tomato sauce and toppings.

The crust of a pizza is plain, though some people prefer to season it with butter, garlic, herbs, or cheese.

In Canada, we have our own "Canadian pizza", which has the topping combination of back bacon, pepperoni, and mushrooms.

C. (Suggested writing)
   1. They were waiting to be rescued. This seemed to be less and less likely to come by. They tried to see if they could salvage anything nearby to keep them warm, as the temperature seemed to be dropping. This made survival even harder.
   2. The players were down by two but they did not lose heart. They believed that there was still time to catch up. As long as they could mount an all-out offence and did not let up, they could crack open the opponents' line of defence, which showed signs of fatigue.
   3. True seals are more streamlined than fur seals; they can swim more effectively over long distances, but they are clumsier on land. Unlike fur seals, they cannot turn their hind flippers downward. This means they have to wriggle with their front flippers and abdominal muscles.

D. (Individual writing)

Review 2

A. 1. friend   2. conceited   3. budgeting
   4. weight   5. pier   6. magpie
   7. beginning   8. breathing

B. 1. NP   2. VP   3. PP   4. NP
   5. PP   6. NP   7. PP   8. VP
   9. VP   10. NP

C. 1. a male voice ; the different shades of sound
   2. will even find ; may have heard
   3. full and rich ; sweet and lyrical
   4. adult male alto ; lower-pitched
   5. to "master the instrument" ; to perform a colourful song
   6. really well ; very patiently

D. (Cross out these words.)
   1. most   2. In my opinion   3. one more time
   4. massively   5. personal   6. already
   7. in her spare time   8. terribly
   9. more ; than Paul's

E. 1. B   2. A   3. C   4. D
   5. F   6. E

F. 1. The script is superb but the acting is lousy. ; but
   2. Mike is still in touch with Neal even though they live far from each other. ; even though
   3. Jake will stay in the neighbourhood as long as his cousin is around. ; as long as
   4. This sauce is delicious because Mom put in a lot of garlic and onions. ; because
   5. The bugs scurried away when we switched on the lights! ; when
   6. Amanda will not leave her room until she has cleaned it inside out. ; until
   7. Come to Halifax to visit me or go to Charlottetown to visit Jen. ; or

G. Alsace is one of the 26 regions of France, bordering Germany and Switzerland. Although it is part of France, it has changed hands between France and Germany many times, which is why its architecture, language, cuisine, music, dress, and even economy have a unique mixture of French and German traditions. As it is a region with a semi-continental climate, Alsace has cold, dry winters and hot summers. You may want to visit Alsace if you are a tree lover, because it contains many forests. The region may also interest you if you are a lover of history, since it was once part of the Holy Roman Empire and is still inhabited by people who speak a dialect of Upper German.

H. (Cross out these words.)
   1. that   4. which   6. that
   7. that   8. whom

I. (Individual writing)

J. 1a. N   b. D   2a. D   b. N
   3a. D   b. N
   4. (Individual writing)

K. (Suggested writing)
He generally does not like movies because they always put him to sleep, which is something he already does ten hours a day. However, he has heard from his friends that this movie, with its well-written script and stunning visual effects, will take his breath away.

1 Creating Images with Words

A. (Suggested answers)
1. stroll ; saunter ; detour
2. munch ; devour ; savour
3. cab ; sedan ; streetcar
4. chilly ; freezing ; frigid
5. baking ; sizzling ; burning
6. motherly ; caring ; compassionate
7. impoverished ; deprived ; unfortunate
8. wealthy; loaded ; abundant
9. fast ; hasty ; swift
10. tower ; skyscraper ; theatre

B. (Individual writing)

C. 1. S   2. S
    3. M   4. S
    5. M   6. M
    7. M   8. S

D. (Individual writing)

E. (Individual writing)

2 Writing at the Sentence Level

A. (Suggested writing)
1. Without making any sound, he lay there for hours.
2. Across the sky, the geese flew in the V-formation.
3. Slithering in the murky water was a dark, shadowy thing.
4. Well into the last quarter, the game was exciting as ever.
5. Against the strong wind and scattered showers, they trudged along.
6. Awed by the pianist's superb performance, the audience applauded excitedly.

B. (Suggested writing)
1. Collecting stamps is my hobby.
2. On the envelope was a beautiful stamp.
3. Through stamp collecting, I get to know many exotic and faraway places.
4. To get stamps seems to be more and more difficult now.
5. Instant messaging is another favourite way of communication.
6. Just like dinosaurs, they will disappear.

C. 1. In front of the altar, the bridegroom waited patiently for the bride.
2. To make this device work, I think we need an additional component.
3. Exercising and getting plenty of rest are what he needs most.
4. Down the meandering river, their boat sailed slowly.
5. To get through the hurdle, the two groups decided to join forces.

D. (Individual writing)

3 Combining Simple Sentences

A. (Suggested writing)
1. Raymond, my teacher's son, often stays behind to help me with math.
2. The Eiffel Tower, one of the most famous structures in the world, welcomes six million visitors every year.

3. We used to have lunch at the Wok, a family restaurant famous for its fried rice.
4. My cousin, a civil engineer, was involved in designing the overpass system.
5. The castle, the landmark of the city, overlooks the entire harbour.

B. (Suggested writing)
1. Compound:
He reached the theatre at about eight but Macy was nowhere to be found.
Complex:
Although he reached the theatre at about eight, Macy was nowhere to be found.
2. Compound:
Keep up the fighting spirit and we still have a chance to avoid being eliminated.
Complex:
Keep up the fighting spirit because we still have a chance to avoid being eliminated.
3. Compound:
The snowstorm is on its way but it will take a day or two to reach this part of the province.
Complex:
Even though the snowstorm is on its way, it will take a day or two to reach this part of the province.
4. Compound:
We did not expect him to arrive a day earlier than scheduled and the set-up was therefore not ready yet.
Complex:
Since we did not expect him to arrive a day earlier than scheduled, the set-up was not ready yet.
5. Compound:
Let me have more data and I will be able to provide you with a more accurate assessment.
Complex:
If you let me have more data, I will be able to provide you with a more accurate assessment.

C. (Suggested writing)
1. Hoping to reach the town in two hours, they sailed along the river.
2. Wanting to know the results first-hand, the students waited anxiously in the classroom.
3. Having played for more than an hour, we were getting tired and decided to go home.
4. Looking for the sign that pointed him to Townsville, he drove on slowly.
5. Not realizing that there was only one minute left, the children were still arguing about who to start first.
6. Speaking to the audience, the mayor reiterated the importance of going green.
7. Noticing that it was getting late, he decided to put up for the night at a nearby motel.
8. Wanting to find out what had happened, the crowd moved closer to the collapsed house.

D. (Individual writing)

4 Paragraphing

A. Drinking tea has been associated with health benefits for centuries, but it is only in recent years that its medicinal properties have been investigated scientifically and proven. // Tea's health benefits are largely due to its high content of catechins. Green tea is the best source of catechins. Catechins are more powerful than vitamins C and E in preventing oxidation from damaging cells. They appear to have other disease-fighting properties too. In fact, studies have found that consuming green tea can reduce risks of cancer. Regular consumption of green and black teas also helps reduce risks of heart disease. The antioxidants in green, black, and oolong teas can help block the oxidation of LDL (bad) cholesterol, increase HDL (good) cholesterol, and improve artery function. // To get the most out of tea drinking, we should drink a cup of tea a few times a day to absorb antioxidants and other healthful plant compounds. The usual amount is three cups per day. Also, we should allow tea to steep for three to five minutes to bring out its catechins, and the best way to get the catechins in tea is to drink it freshly brewed. Tea can impede the absorption of iron from fruits and vegetables, but adding lemon or milk will counteract this problem.

B. (Suggested writing)
It is believed that tea drinking originated from China. It was the second emperor of China, Shen Nung, who discovered tea.

One day, Emperor Shen Nung was sipping a cup of hot water in his garden when a tea leaf dropped into his cup. He liked the flavour of the water with the leaf in it, and from then onward, he put tea leaves in the hot water he drank.

Soon, his people followed suit and put tea leaves in hot water. Tea drinking became more and more popular. Some even added onion, ginger, or spices to make medicinal beverages.

C. (Suggested writing)
Most people think that afternoon tea is synonymous with high tea. In fact, they are two entirely different things.

Afternoon tea began in the mid-1800s. In those days, lunch was served at noon but dinner was not eaten until late at night. A noblewoman, the Duchess of Bedford, found herself hungry during those long afternoon hours and so she started having a tray of tea with bread and butter served to her in the mid-afternoon.

Soon, she began to invite other ladies to join her. Without realizing it, the Duchess of Bedford was setting the trend of having afternoon tea for the upper-class women.

High tea, on the other hand, was served around six in the evening. And although high tea sounds classy, it actually consisted of a full dinner for the common people. Tea was still served, but there would also be meats, fish or eggs, cheese, bread and butter, and cake.

5 Building Paragraphs

A. (Suggested writing)
1. The moose is a big animal.
2. Using the maple leaf as a symbol of Canada goes back a long way.
3. There are different theories as to how hockey came about in Canada.
B. (Individual writing)
C. (Individual writing)

6 Taking Notes

A. (Individual writing)
B. (Individual writing)

7 Developing a Writing Plan

A. 1. A   2. A   3. B
    4. C   5. A
B. (Suggested writing)
1. a narrative that informs and entertains
2. a description that creates a mental picture for the reader
3. a piece that explains how and why sports players can be role models
4. an informational piece that teaches how to live green and encourages this lifestyle
C. (Individual writing)
D. (Individual writing)

8 Guiding Questions

A. (Individual writing)
B. (Individual writing)

9 Formal and Informal Writing

A. (Individual writing)
B. (Individual writing)
C. (Individual writing)

10 Descriptive Writing (1)

A. 1. S   2. S
    3. O   4. O
    5. S   6. S
B. Shania Twain is a remarkable Canadian singer and songwriter who has enjoyed immense success in the country and pop music genres. Her third album "Come on Over" is the biggest-selling album of all time by a female artist, and the seventh biggest-selling album in music history, and she is the only female artist to have three albums certified Diamond by the RIAA.

Twain's debut album in 1993 was unsatisfactory as she was forced by her record company to work with Nashville songwriters, and she only got to co-write one of the songs, and felt that the album was not really her own.

Things changed when the legendary rock producer Robert "Mutt" Lange heard Shania's original songs and singing and thought she held promise. He offered to produce her and to write songs with her. After many telephone conversations, they met in person at Nashville's Fan Fair in June 1993. Soon their professional relationship took a romantic turn, and they were married on December 28, 1993.

Lange and Twain instantly formed a successful partnership,

and Twain has often commented that the reason they work so well is they are so different; after all, Lange is 17 years older than Twain.

C. Hair and Facial Features:
bearded ; blonde ; curly ; fresh-faced ; greasy ; handsome ; with rosy cheeks ; with thick lips ; fluffy ; clean-shaven ; with pitcher ears
Age:
elderly ; youngish ; youthful ; teenage ; middle-aged
Build:
chubby ; muscular ; shapely ; skinny ; lanky
Personality:
generous ; sweet ; hard-working ; helpful ; intelligent ; musical
Voice:
booming ; coarse
Dress:
elegant ; fashionable ; trendy

D. (Individual writing)

11 Descriptive Writing (2)

A. (Individual writing)
B. (Individual writing)
C. 2 ; 2 ; 2 ; 2 ;
1 ; 3 ; 1 ; 1 ;
2 ; 2 ; 2 ; 2
D. (Individual writing)

12 Factual Writing

A. (Suggested writing)
1. located in Toronto, Ontario
2. Canada's largest museum of human cultures and natural history
3. more than six million items from dinosaurs to Canadian history
4. officially opened on March 14, 1914
5. original building designed by Frank Darling and John A. Pearson
6. museum's site chosen for proximity to University of Toronto
7. established in 1912 by provincial government
8. operated by University of Toronto until 1955
9. still shares expertise and resources with University of Toronto
10. recently completed major renovation project called Renaissance ROM
B. (Suggested writing)
Opening Paragraph:
Located in the Gulf of St. Lawrence on Canada's east coast, Prince Edward Island is the smallest of the Canadian provinces both in size and population.
Body Paragraphs:
The province is named in honour of Edward, Duke of Kent (father of Queen Victoria) in 1799, and is made famous by *Anne of Green Gables* published in 1908. In addition to lobsters, mussels, and seafood, which are readily available, the islanders eat lots of potatoes since they are grown in the province.

PEI has Charlottetown as its capital city, and offers plenty to do: delicious seafood suppers, uncrowded beaches, and more than a dozen golf courses. There are about 1.2 million visitors annually.
Concluding Paragraph:
Although the island is separated from mainland Canada, New Brunswick, and Nova Scotia by the Northumberland Strait, it is connected to New Brunswick by the Confederation Bridge (12.9 km), which opened in 1997.

13 Basic Proofreading and Editing (1)

A. 1.   2. ✗
3.   4.
5. ✗   6. ✗
7.   8. ✗
9.   10. ✗
11. ✗
B. (Suggested writing)
1. The weather is fine, so we can go hiking this afternoon.
2. It doesn't make sense to me: there is no mention of the procedure.
3. Wait here and don't touch anything.
4. If you don't go, I won't go either.
5. Many think that he is a capable leader but I don't think so.
6. Let's make a checklist so that we can be sure that we won't leave anything important behind.
7. The police interrogated him for hours because they suspected that he was the mastermind.
C. 1. Toronto, which is the capital of Ontario, is the largest city in Canada. It is home to the world's tallest building (the CN Tower at 553.33 metres) and the world's longest street starts at the city's lakeshore (Yonge Street at 1896 kilometres). It also has one of the world's most diverse and multicultural populations. Did you also know that there are more people living in Toronto than in Canada's four Atlantic provinces combined?
2. What game is played on horseback? It's polo. Polo is believed to have originated among the Iranian tribes, between 521 and 485 BCE. A polo game is played by two teams, each comprising four players. The polo field is 300 yards long, and either 160 yards or 150 yards wide. On each side of the field is a goal: the two goalposts are eight yards apart. The two opposing teams are to score the most goals by hitting the ball through the goal. There are two mounted umpires on the field and a referee standing on the sidelines.
D. (Suggested writing)
Nova Scotia – Latin for New Scotland – is located on Canada's southeastern coast. Although Nova Scotia is the second smallest province, it is the most populous province in the Maritimes. Its capital, Halifax, is the economic and cultural centre of the region.

Some people believe that the Vikings may have settled in Nova Scotia at some time, though there is little evidence of this. The only authenticated Viking settlement in North America is L'Anse aux Meadows: it establishes the fact that Vikings explored North America 500 years before Christopher Columbus.

There are other stories about early explorations of Nova

Scotia, such as the one about the Italian explorer John Cabot. While there is some debate over where he landed, it is believed that he visited present-day Cape Breton in 1497.

14 Basic Proofreading and Editing (2)

A. 1. There were quite a few people watching when the accident occurred.
2. He doesn't seem to understand how serious that can be.
4. Everyone is having a great time at the party.
5. Neither he nor the chairman is aware of the development.
6. Any one of them is capable of helping you with the project.
8. The police were trying to disperse the crowd but without much success.
9. There are a couple of matters that we need to resolve.

B. (Suggested writing)
1. I couldn't sleep and woke up at 3:00 a.m.
2. You should not repeat the same mistake.
3. They agree with one another.
4. The troop was surrounded by the enemy.
5. Jason wants to study medicine and be a doctor in future.
6. I don't see any reason for an honest person to do it that way.
7. He kept telling me about it because he was worried that I did not believe him.

C. The polar bear lives in the Arctic region. It is well-adapted to its habitat with its thick blubber and fur, which insulate it against the bitter cold. The polar bear's fur appears white or cream-coloured. This helps camouflage it from its prey. The polar bear hunts well on land and on the sea ice, as well as in the water.

Polar bears use sea ice as a platform to hunt seals, which are the mainstay of their diet. The destruction of their habitat on the Arctic ice, believed to be caused by global warming, is threatening their survival. In fact, some scientists warn that polar bears may become extinct within the century.

Most adult male polar bears weigh from 300 to 600 kilograms and measure 2.4 to 2.6 metres in length. According to Guinness World Records 2006, the largest polar bear was one shot in Kotzebue Sound, Alaska in 1960 – it weighed 880 kg and was 3.38 m in length! Female polar bears are generally about half the size of males.

D. The polar bear is the most <u>carniverous</u> [carnivorous] member of the bear family, and the one that is most likely to prey on human beings for food. Although it feeds mainly on seals, it eats virtually anything it can kill: birds, rodents, beluga whales, and young <u>walnuses</u> [walruses], and very <u>occassionally</u> [occasionally], other polar bears as well. Polar bears are <u>enormusly</u> [enormously] strong and powerful. They also <u>haunt</u> [hunt] very <u>efficently</u> [efficiently] on land due to their speed. In fact, they can easily outrun a <u>humen</u> [human]. They are, however, not as fast as caribou and musk oxen, which

is why they subsist almost entirely on seals and young walruses. After all, seals and young walruses are much easier <u>pray</u> [prey].

Polar bears are <u>excellant</u> [excellent] swimmers and can often be seen in open waters far from land. <u>Resently</u> [Recently], polar bears have undertaken longer than usual swims to find prey because of the melting of ice <u>flows</u> [floes]. In 2005, there were four recorded drownings as a result of the unusually large ice pack regression.